The Deer Park

In sixteenth century England, as in the 20th and 21st centuries, displaced persons were a not uncommon sight; the difference was that these were made homeless in their own land, by a royal edict, and without redress to courts or legal aid. Thousands of monks and nuns became homeless when Henry VIII suppressed the monasteries. This story, which is fiction but could easily have been fact, imagines how a handful of them survived, by various means, in the face of danger and hardship. In many cases their faith sustained them – but for some physical love, for others special skills, enabled them to start a new life. With one or two exceptions the characters are imaginary, but the events historically based, and most of the buildings (or ruins) can still be identified today. Dorsley Abbey never existed, but National Trust members and others may be able to relate the Deer Park to Newark Park in Gloucestershire, which was indeed built by Sir Nicholas Poyntz.

The Deer Park

A story of displaced persons
in 16th century England

Barbara Hooper

JLF MARKETING

First published in Great Britain 2007

© Barbara Hooper 2007

The right of Barbara Hooper to be identified as the author of this work is asserted. No part of this publication may be reproduced or transmitted by any means or in any form without the prior permission of the author.

Cover design based on a painting *Monks in Meditation* by Etienne Jeaurat (1699–1789)

Set in Galliard by Bookcraft, Stroud, Gloucestershire
Printed and bound by C P I Antony Rowe, Eastbourne, East Sussex

Published by JLF Marketing, Parlour Farm House, Bisley, Glos. GL6 7BH

ISBN 0-9541806-1-5
ISBN13 978-0-9541806-1-4

This is in gratitude to those people who taught me to appreciate the written record of local history, and the visual record of archaeology

HISTORICAL BACKGROUND

In the years 1536 to 1539 a shadow fell over England, and particularly over its religious houses, as the king fought a prolonged war of attrition against them in his determination to break away from the Roman Catholic Church and set up a Protestant church with himself at its head. His motivation was clear: to legalise his divorce from Katharine of Aragon, and to take Anne Boleyn as his second wife with a wife still living.

Many religious houses throughout the country, large and small, became victims of Henry's ambition. For some it was simply a matter of curtailing their practices. Others which failed to conform were arbitrarily closed down. A few, offering active rather than passive resistance, suffered appalling violence, even murder, and the wholesale demolition of their buildings. The nationwide suppression of the monasteries, as the onslaught came to be known, was carried out under the supervision of the Lord Privy Seal, Thomas Cromwell, sometimes called the Hammer of the Monks.

Some aristocrats connected to the Court, or landowners highly favoured by the king, were granted the right to dispose of whole monastic lands and buildings. Certain abbeys, among them Tewkesbury and Malmesbury, became parish churches. Some achieved the status of cathedrals. Many survived only as roofless ruins ("bare ruined choirs where once the sweet birds sang.") Some were obliterated as if they had never been. In total some 5000 monks and 2000 nuns were rendered homeless.

This story envisages the possible fate of a few of the monastic people who survived.

I

BROTHER LEO

There are the anchorites or hermits, who have come through the test of living in a monastery for a long time, and have passed beyond the first fervour of monastic life … . Self-reliant now, without the support of another, they are ready with God's help to grapple single-handed with the vices of body and mind.

The Rule of St Benedict in English, chapter one

This is my garden, and no one comes here unless I unlock the gate. For seven years I have planted and weeded and harvested, not for *them*, but for God. The produce I give to the poor who come to the gate to collect it, keeping back a little for myself. Some gets taken by the deer and the rabbits, but I do not grudge them their share. As far as possible the garden does not yield up fruit or vegetables or honey for *them*.

Laus Deo. This is my garden, and I am working for my God. How long have you been here, they ask. I do not count in years, but in growing seasons – perhaps ten seasons, since the brutal men came to desecrate our Abbey. Life was good before that. We had a joyful community, observing the Rule, illuminating most skilfully the documents men brought us, a little teaching, a little medicine. And my task? Looking after the gardens of our glorious Abbey, providing the Brothers with herbs and roots, apples and grain and eggs, yes, and fish too from the ponds we created downstream from the garden. I had my bees and my geese for company as well as the younger Brothers to laugh and help me. Life was good until the pagans came.

Here we are on the very edge of the Wold, where it is bleak in winter and windswept even in summer. The soil is poorer than it was at the Abbey, and what trees there are crouch against the wind. One or two of them at the big house bring me small comforts: Ellen the housekeeper brings soup or a newly baked loaf. Elizabeth in the dairy sometimes – not often – remembers me with curds or cheese when she has a surplus. Robert in the stables, once a good Catholic altar boy and a novice who some of us hoped would rise in the Order, fetches me a little ale from time to time. Otherwise I have almost nothing to do with them, except when Sir Nicholas conducts his visitors round the formal garden and shows off my planting, but without mentioning me to them. At those times I must not be seen or heard.

These people are Protestants. They have no chapel, hear no Mass, observe Sundays very laxly. I have even noted deer sports and hunting with dogs on a Sunday. As for me, I say the Mass daily to myself, and keep the Rule as best I can. I would retreat altogether as a hermit if I could, but legally I must live here and look after the renegades' gardens. I tell myself I am working for God, not for them. And in secret places, hidden shrines among the shrubs, I have my icons. These I brought from the Abbey to save them from desecration, perhaps even total destruction. So far no one knows they are here, and with God's help I intend to keep it that way.

I have to admit the house is handsome. They call it a hunting lodge, but what true hunting lodge has bedrooms and a banqueting hall and stands four stories high surrounded by a park of a thousand acres? On the roof stands not the Cross of Christendom, but a gilded phoenix, a pagan symbol if ever there was one. Below gleams the great coloured window which people come from far to admire, but that faces east and there are only a few small windows on the west side, looking out over my garden.

The formal garden is my responsibility too, but I am not proud of it. It is in the artificial French fashion, not a good plain English garden but knots and twirls making a pattern, low-cut hedges of box and yew and French lavender, sometimes called santolina. In between: not pleasing turf, but paths of gravel, quite unnatural. I was instructed in the art of topiary and parterre by Master Etienne, who came from France to lay out some of the great gardens at Longleat and Berkeley and Sudeley. This must be kept trimmed and weed-free, just so, to please *them*. The formal garden extends along the west side of the lodge, so that afternoon and evening sun reaches it and makes strange shadows of the dwarf hedges. At first I found it difficult to keep the pattern exact, but now the plants are settled in and I have only to trim them every few weeks. In the centre is a roundel with a sundial (I would call it a Mass dial, but this would enrage the anti-Catholics.) The lowcut evergreens radiate out from this, as if spokes in a wheel. When women walk along these narrow walkways, as they do from time to time, they find it tiresome whisking their skirts between the miniature hedges. This does not worry me; I prefer them not to come.

Very few people here take the trouble to talk to me. Why should they bother with an old man, a Papist, one whom they regard as illiterate? There is a young woman, a lady in waiting to relatives of the Poyntzes. She is little more than a girl, and she spends time in the stables, loving horses, and in the garden with me, loving the plants, the birds and the small wild creatures that live in the garden. When she comes to visit from Yate Court she looks for me in the herb garden, or among the bee skeps. I lose my habitual depression when I hear her musical voice: "Brother Leo, may I come and talk to you a little? You are not at your prayers, are you?" They call her Lady Felicity, and believe me she is well named.

Sir Nicholas's wife comes now and then to cut flowers or collect herbs. She calls out to me, using the pretentious Italian name she affects: "Father Leonardo, where are you? Come here and help me choose flowers for the banquet. Tomorrow lords and ladies from the Court will be here to watch the hunting and ride in the park. Everything must be just so, even the flower arrangements. They must not think we are country bumpkins because we are so far from London."

I know exactly what she means. These stiffnecked renegade nobles will stay in the lap of luxury at Yate Court, waited on by forty servants Sir Nicholas keeps there just to impress guests from London. Once, they tell me, the King himself stayed there on one of his royal progresses. The whole house was renovated to please him: an audience chamber, a suite of rooms for courtiers, newly embroidered tapestries, portraits specially commissioned of the king's ancestors. A fortune was spent on fripperies for a one-week stay. The Poyntzes are mostly in London, coming down to Gloucestershire for what they call country air, and this place is no more than a weekend fancy. Not that I blame them for wanting to impress the king. They all must do that if they are to keep their heads on their shoulders in these turbulent times.

Yate Court is more beautiful than here. Pinkish red bricks cluster around a courtyard. Stables, bakehouse and brewery form the sides of the courtyard. There is a moat, with a drawbridge and a tree-lined avenue leading in through the walled garden. I know this, because I was taken there once – once only – to advise them about restocking the herb garden and fish ponds. But the setting is quite flat and nothing much compared with this place. Here we have cliffs dropping down to the Severn Vale, with a view one might wish to die for. We have rolling acres of parkland, and a great artificial lake. Fruit grows in the fighouse and the pomegranate arbour. Under the giant chestnuts I can see sheep and the deer herd which gives the estate its name: Deer Park. I could love this place but for the dreadful circumstances which brought me here, and make it impossible for me to escape. Barely twelve miles away was my real and spiritual home, the Community of St Mary the Virgin, where we kept the true faith. Nothing remains. If I were to ride over there now I would see only a few ruined foundations, uncared for and forlorn. And two men chiefly are to blame for this latest act of vandalism: Sir Nicholas Poyntz and his chamberlain, Tobias Fenton.

Fenton rules the household here. He arrives from Yate Court ahead of Sir Nicholas and gives unnecessary orders to the Staff, who know perfectly well what is required. There are seven of us here all through the year. In summer and autumn the house must be prepared for up to twenty guests who may stay a night or two, or simply ride away after feasting. The work that goes on to entertain these few visitors can scarcely be believed. The drive up from the Vale must be freshly sanded and raked, the stables made ready for two dozen horses.

Ellen the housekeeper is mistress of the house until Lady Poyntz comes. Ellen orders the maids of the chamber to clean, heat and arrange the bedrooms, although they may not be used. The rooms are cold and perhaps rather damp even in summer, she tells me, so buckets of hot faggots are carried up two flights of stairs. The withdrawing room must be heated too, with its huge open fire. At times I am ordered to help fetch logs from the park; they are dragged on a kind of sledge by the horses which are kept here all year as pack animals. The great kitchen, below ground level, is used only when guests come, and the Poyntzes bring their own kitchen staff – ten of them – to set up the feasts for these occasions.

Deer from the park are hunted as soon as the guests gather, ánd the lords and ladies gather on the roof to watch the deer coursing. To me it is a barbarous practice, these shy delicate animals, God's creatures as much as we are, being driven to death by the deerhounds. Their cries and struggles are pitiful to see and hear. Immediately a deer is killed the carcase is dragged to the kitchen to be roasted whole on a spit turned by Edwin the scullion. When the guests have had their fill of watching these animals being cruelly hunted they retire from the roof to the upper rooms for possets of French wine, then to the banqueting hall for the feast which (they tell me) is the main purpose of their visit. Great platters of food are carried up from the kitchen, venison, wild boar, swans (all from the estate), enormous loaves, puddings, bowls of fruit. The feasting may last for hours.

While this is happening the servants who have ridden over as grooms or baggage carriers from Yate Court expect to be fed in the kitchens. One or two of them may come to speak to me, for I have been a fixture at Deer Park for many years. "Are you still here, Brother Leo? We had thought you gone long ago." But we have almost nothing in common, these city-bred serving men and me.

Likewise some of the guests may stroll in the gardens next day, and compliment Sir Nicholas on his roses or his topiary. This is his particular pride, the latest fashion and something to show off to people from London who have not seen anything like it before. This is a garden within a garden, very orderly, a place of light and shade, and it reminds me at certain times of our shady cloister at the Abbey. The smaller alcoves opening off the main topiary quadrangle are not unlike the monks' cells, and at dusk I can imagine myself back in that sacred place. It is my task to clip the yew and box bushes to fanciful shapes, gathered around a paved court as if they were sculptors' models, or lords and ladies in a stately dance. We have a dozen chessmen, a bear, a swan, hawks and doves, as well as ornamental spirals, cones and spheres, and they need constant clipping to keep their shape. In the first place I had some difficulty in knowing what they should resemble, but Robert the stableman and Davy the park shepherd gave me good advice. Indeed without Davy's shearing tools the work would be far harder. They are good friends, and lend me a hand when they can escape from their own duties.

The heretic nobles may admire the topiary and the knot garden, but they have no idea of the work involved in creating these to please the few. Not only the shearing requires skill, but also the manuring, the raking around the shapes, the weeding among the paving stones. To me it is not true gardening, but artifice. However I must admit there is satisfaction in seeing the clipped yew bushes turn gradually into knights or deerhounds or peacocks. The colours vary too, for we have golden yew and golden privet in among the dark green rosemary and box, and I can feel I am creating a painted picture. It is for my pleasure more than for any of these Court aristocrats, and I am offering the garden to God. Nonetheless it makes me proud, heaven forgive my sinfulness, when a non -believer speaks well of my work.

I am pleased too, God forgive me, when the couples walk in the pleached lime allée or stroll around the orchard. A few even visit the potager to see where my vegetables flourish. But there is no denying the chief admiration of Sir Nicholas and his Godless guests is reserved for the parterre, that geometrical fancy of dwarf bushes and hedges imagined and controlled by me.

The household servants slave for a day or two, then the party is over and the guests disappear, taking with them a topic for conversation at Court or a witticism or two when they return to London. They may never come again – Court favourites change as often as the weather. But we cannot leave, the seven of us who are bound here, legally and morally, as surely as any slaves.

My great comfort is young Robert, who comes and goes as a groom whenever he pleases: he is a favourite of Lady Poyntz. She introduces him to her Court circle and orders him to escort the ladies riding in the park. But I know Robert is not one of them. He was at the Abbey for five years, and he keeps me in touch with some of my former fellow religious, those who survived; he tells me how they are faring, and gives them reports of my wellbeing (if you can call it that.) Robert is my link with the outside world and what remains of our Cistercian Order. I joined it as a novice monk forty years ago, and my heart still belongs to Our Lord and the Order. May God forgive my neglect.

II

ABBOT GODFREY

1535: From Godfrey le Verbier, Abbot of Abbey Dorsley, to the Abbot of Citeaux in Burgundy

Written on the Feast Day of Pope Gregory the Great, Bishop of Rome and Teacher of the Faith, the third day of September, in the Year of Our Lord 1535.

Reverend Father in God,

I write to give you my annual report on the affairs of the Cistercian community of St Mary the Virgin at Abbey Dorsley in the West of England. It pleases me to write on the Feast of St Gregory the Great, he who sent the Blessed Augustine to convert the people of England; and more especially because he devised our system of plainsong psalmody, which we sing here in the Dorian Mode – as I hope in due course you will be able to hear and judge for yourself, Reverend Father.

It has taken me years to bring this wayward house to some kind of discipline, so that your representative can visit from France and find here a community to be proud of. I don't take all the credit for this, but things were in a sorry state when I was ordered here from Caen and told to drive out the evil weeds that had taken root here and infected the whole community. I found a group of brothers who were little better than beer swilling roughnecks, so I soon sent them packing. I can assure you now the Rule of St Benedict is properly and strictly observed and the brothers know what is expected of them. Among our 24 brethren we have some extremely skilled illuminators and one or two who sing passably well in the choir.

The Obedientiaries are well trained, since most of them came with me from France. You will recall that I hand-picked those who were to take office as Prior, Sacrist, Treasurer, Steward, Chamberlain and Almoner. We are fortunate to have found a few resident here for many years who also know their business.

I rely heavily on the wisdom and expertise of the Guestmaster, Walter, who was here when I came and acts as deputy to our beloved Guilbert of Normandy when I am obliged to travel on Abbey business. We entertain many guests here, travellers on the road to Gloucester, Hereford or Worcester, King's messengers, and pilgrims who are touring the shrines of the west of England. They may arrive here from Glastonbury or Hailes, from Malmesbury or Winchcombe.

Those who have been to Glastonbury speak with awe of the Blessed Thorn – some even have seen it blossom at Christmas, as I myself did once on my way from France. It was an experience never to be forgotten, the outburst of sacred white flowers against the snow on that lonely hill, and certainly miraculous. I do not doubt the Blessed Joseph of Arimathaea brought it here on his wanderings, a slip from the Crown of Thorns itself. That it should bloom on Christ's birthday is proof enough of its sanctity, and I hear of miracles wrought for the sick by this miraculous tree. Some relate the Hill of Glastonbury to Calvary itself.

Other guests educate us with their account of the sacred phial of the most Holy Blood brought to Hailes by Edmund of Cornwall after the Crusades. You will recall, Father in God, that the abbey was founded by Richard the first Earl of Cornwall to fulfil a vow he made after escaping from a shipwreck off the Scilly Isles (where many of our fellow countrymen have perished on those terrible rocks, coming by sea from France). Hailes was most liberally endowed by Earl Richard, ánd his son Edmund, the second earl, an equally pious man, brought back the Holy Blood from Jerusalem.

I am told it was blessed by the Patriarch of Jerusalem, who became Our Holy Father Urban IV, and it is preserved in a shrine circled by seven stone hearts. So you will see that in this part of England there are many objects to be venerated, not least our own lace fragment of Our Lady's veil, which is guarded in a silver casket. Forgive me if I am repeating matters you already know of.

Walter sees to it that our more privileged guests are well accommodated, well fed and wined from the Cellar, and if their rank merits it he may bring them to be introduced to me. Those of the highest rank may stay in my own house. Of course, Reverend Father, I do not allow these visits to interfere with my Abbatial duties.

Brother Wilfrid runs the mill and Brother Anselm the bakehouse. I leave it to them, having no knowledge of grinding or breadmaking. Nor do I wish to: these are domestic matters best left to the brethren who come from English yeoman stock. Brother Cuthbert is our cook, and I have no complaint about our meals. Indeed I daresay we eat better than many monastic communities. Brother Joseph and Brother Vincent attend to the carpentry and the ironworking. Brother Daniel has more than normal artistic talent, so I encourage him to spend much time working on his manuscripts. Indeed I am pleased to report that a scroll of his was presented lately to the Bishop. Brother Stephen weaves our habits, and Brother Leo provides produce from the garden and the poultry yard and fishponds. They are all conscientious members of the Order who know their place.

We have two elderly brothers in the Infirmary. I do not expect Brother Adam to live much longer; he came to this House of Our Lady as a boy, and for many years he was our Novicemaster. When I came here he chose to relinquish these tasks, but our relations remain cordial and he hears Mass daily from me or one of the senior members of our Order. Brother Peter is a greater concern to me. Latterly he has become some-what feeble-minded and can be found wandering in the grounds at inappropriate times, talking to himself and behaving strangely. I have deputed one of the younger men, Brother Septimus, to keep an eye on him and let me know if he appears likely to endanger himself or others. Brother Theodore, our Infirmarian, attends to those with temporary illnesses.

We have four novices at present: John, Robert, Edmund and Geoffrey. I would not say any of them are wholly committed to the life of the Cloister, but they are willing workers and to tell the truth we need young hands and brains. When they are not studying they assist with the day-to-day chores of the Abbey. All of them are from local families except Robert, who came to us from Worcester. I find him inclined to rebelliousness, and I have more than once had occasion to rebuke him for idle speech, which of course is one of the evils our Blessed St Bernard of Clairvaux most enjoined us against. Also I fancy he has a roving eye.

Geoffrey is our youngest novice, and he finds scholarship difficult. However he perseveres at his studies, and he is now allowed to read aloud from Holy Scriptures at mealtimes; although I take care to see it is not too often. His reading improves slowly.

From France I sent especially for our scholars, our Novicemaster, our Cellarer and our Infirmarian. For the rest the daily tasks of the monastery are carried out by lay brothers and workers from the village. They work in the Bakehouse, the Brewery and the Kitchens and help on the farms at harvest or sheep-shearing time. They are cheerful and willing workers,

11

though of course illiterate, and I do not detect ill feeling between the monastic community and the lay helpers as there might well be in a household less strictly run than mine. We are largely self-sufficient, but beer is provided by the village (these poor souls look to us for spiritual guidance and teaching, and in return we expect them to supply us with those extra comforts which are outside our capacity.) Wine reaches me from France; this I sometimes share with a few senior members of the community. Before I arrived there was some eating of meat, but I soon put a stop to that.

St Benedict enjoins us to offer hospitality to travellers who come to our door, and to provide relief for the old, sick and poor. This we do within reason; ours is a small community and not over-wealthy. But Brother Almoner attends to these matters. One of our most important duties is to offer up prayers for our founder, Sir Thomas de Berkeley. You will recall there were tiresome disputes over ownership of land which had been (in my judgment) properly made over to us by his ancestor Sir Roger and confirmed by Queen Maud of blessed memory, on condition that we said a daily Mass for the repose of the soul of her father King Henry. These disputes were finally settled, though not without financial burdens to those involved. It is sad that there should have been wrangling over land to be dedicated for the building of God's House. Sir Thomas laid the first stone of this foundation, in 1139. So we look ahead to celebrating our 400th anniversary shortly, and we respectfully ask that you, Reverend Father, may pay us a ceremonial visit on that joyful occasion. There are plans in hand for much special rejoicing, though I hope we shall not forget our vows.

I have the honour to report that under my supervision the buildings and the treasures they contain are exceedingly well cared for. The sacred reliquary holding a piece of lace from Our Lady's robe is placed by the high altar, secured with chains, and no pilgrim may approach unless he is escorted by one of the Community. It would be a great honour for us all if you could make a Visitation here on the Feast of the Annunciation of Our Lord to the Blessed Virgin Mary. At the Mass of Our Lady we carry the reliquary in solemn procession to the Abbey Church, and there hold it up for the congregation to venerate. Many devout come from far and wide (and especially from Brittany and Cornwall) to take part in this ancient ceremony.

In the Lady Chapel close by we venerate a statue of Our Lady carved in Flemish oak, said to be more than one hundred years old, possibly brought here by Flemish weavers. Alongside is the chantry chapel dedicated to our founder, who is remembered on his natal day and the day of his death with requiem masses. The foundation of the Abbey is celebrated in July, appropriately (we think) on the festal day of the Blessed Benedict.

Here too is the shrine enclosing the bones of St Guelph, an as yet little-known saint who performed miracles here and on the borders of Wales. His feast day is in October, and we arrange a special Mass for local people to draw attention to his story. We are doing all we can to make England and Wales aware of St Guelph's miraculous life.

We greatly revere these sacred objects and also our silver chalice and paten, brought here from France by me as a gift to Abbey Dorsley from my former community in Caen. As you can imagine much of our income comes naturally from common pilgrims. They come in flocks and droves to see our relics and our holy statues, some on foot, some by horse, some in wagons, and it keeps two or three brothers busy guiding them around the abbey and collecting their charitable offerings. Without our holy objects of veneration we should be considerably poorer, and I assure you we offer a much appreciated service to these simple but godly believers. It is all extra work for us, so that at times some of the brethren feel an urge to turn the pilgrims away, but our Heavenly Father enjoins us to care for the humble and meek, and so we do. St Benedict I believe would approve our hospitality.

I must give some account of our stewardship of the lands given to us by the de Berkeley family and other lesser benefactors. From them we hold some 500 acres of woodland, pasture, water meadows and ploughland. Most of this land is worked by tenant farmers whose chief commodity is wool from our famous

Cotswold sheep. The wool is fine staple and sells well at market, as well as supplying Brother Stephen with all he needs for his weaving. To the local landowners we sell timber, hay and grain. The villagers come here to get their corn ground at our mill. Some graze their sheep on our land: of course you would not expect us to keep livestock, but if important guests ask for meat, I understand Brother Cuthbert can get supplies from the village. We do have a few pigs, geese and waterfowl, but no more than help to supplement our winter fare. There is no waste here, I assure you. In all I believe our income from the Abbey lands may reach a little over £200 in a year. This is made public at Michaelmas; the revenue we receive from pilgrims I do not make public, as these are donations, not earned income. (I am sure you would approve this, Reverend Father.) Most of the pilgrims ask us to say Masses for them, and this we do most earnestly. The villagers also, devout but unlettered people, attend Mass here daily and make their offerings also. One or two local lads have been trained to serve us as altar boys, lay vergers and the like. I do not think it would be boastful to say we have been an educating and civilising influence among them.

Reverend Father in God, I assure you this is a devout and diligent community. Though we are few, we feel we are a tribute to the Order. I am a little anxious that one or two of the brothers may not perfectly follow the Rule, but because they work hard and are useful to us I rebuke them only mildly. Brother Leonard our herbalist is an independent spirit, apt to make his own decisions, though Godly, and on occasion the jovial nature of Brother Wilfrid, our miller, gives me cause for anxiety. However I submit that under my charge Abbey Dorsley fulfils its monastic duty as you would wish it to, thanks be to God.

I must report on my visits to sister houses at Kingswood and Tintern, where I was most kindly received by my fellow Heads of House. Rest assured, Reverend Father, that I do not travel ostentatiously, as some of our Order do. I take with me three lay servants, a groom and a small retinue of horses. I carry with me a few gifts of Cotswold woollen cloth and illuminated Psalters worked at Abbey Dorsley, in case I should need to present rewards or special offerings. My fellow Abbots entertain me generously, and I would hope to return this hospitality in future years.

During my stay at both Houses we had earnest discussion about the present state of the Cistercian Order in England. There is talk of members of our Order, along with other monastic and conventual communities, having to take an oath of allegiance to the King in respect of his new status as Supreme Head of the Church in England. We do not believe this will affect our own discipline, and as yet no such requirement has been imposed upon us. While we recognise the King's desire for partial independence from the Vatican, it would seem that he still supports the Church of Rome in other respects. The main change we anticipate is the official recognition of Master William Tyndale's version of the Bible in English. He is of course a local man, born in Gloucestershire, but we must be cautious in accepting this major reformation (a word that is being bandied around rather loosely at the present time.) As you may know he fled to Germany where his New Testament has been copied; I understand it is all handwritten and is being secretly brought to these islands. Of course I realise it is not approved by the senior clerics, but I do truly believe it will bring the word of God to non-believers who have little knowledge of Latin. Sadly, their numbers grow year by year, and there is (I am told) a clear demand from the lay people for an English Bible. For myself, I am thankful that the Mass continues to be celebrated in Latin and we may worship traditionally. I am optimistic that this so-called reformation will come about peacefully and gradually.

Privately we must deplore the untimely and cruel end of the good Sir Thomas More, eight weeks ago, and say Masses daily for his soul. I say this to you in confidence, Reverend Father, for it would be unwise to make our feelings known publicly.

It does not seem to us likely that the new Lutheran and Calvinistic movements now arriving from the Continent will gain much sympathy here, and we do not expect any positive moves to restrict our way of life or curtail our Catholic rites.

However my fellow Abbots and I feel it prudent to keep abreast of developments at Court. You will know of the power wielded by Master Thomas Cromwell, the Lord Privy Seal. He is very close to the King, and was formerly Solicitor to the great Cardinal Wolsey. In this capacity he was charged with closing some of the lesser monasteries, but of course none that came within your purview, Reverend Father in God. I am told it was he who introduced the Act of Parliament by which the Lord Bishops are no longer required to hand over their first year's income to His Holiness the Pope.

Now it is rumoured (I do not trust rumours, but I feel it my duty to make you aware of them) that Master Cromwell is to be appointed the King's Vicar General (a title we believed belonged only to the Cardinal) with powers to visit and reform all the Abbeys in England. I suspend judgement on this threat to our independence until more evidence is forthcoming. This Lord Privy Seal is reported to be a ruthless man with strong leanings towards the Calvinist and Lutheran movements on the Continent. I have also heard the name of the diabolical Italian writer and diplomat, Niccolo Macchiavelli (now dead, I am glad to say) linked to that of Master Thomas Cromwell. Pray Heaven our Order does not come under these malign influences.

I feel it only right to report to you, dear Father in God, of repercussions that may arise from the Reformation in this country; however minor, we must take note of such changes, and be always vigilant.

Reverend Father Superior, I send my most obedient and respectful salutations to you and to all my superiors at the Mother House. Deo gratias et pax vobiscum in aeternam.

Godfrey, Abbot by the Grace of God and Father Superior of the Abbey of St Mary the Virgin.

Abbey Dorsley, England, this 3rd day of September, 1535.

When he had signed, sealed and handed over the document for delivery by the next messenger travelling to the Cistercian mother house, Godfrey sent for his Prior, Guilbert.

"I have written my annual report to Citeaux. I felt it would be remiss of me not to mention the anti-clerical movement and the New Learning, so-called. I doubt if we are much threatened here, and if it comes to it I am quite prepared to defy all these new notions. But should I take the community into my confidence? Is it likely they will find out about all this political chicanery from outsiders?"

Guilbert hesitated before replying.

"We have every confidence in you, Father. But it is possible they hear news of doings at Court from pilgrims, or travellers staying here. You know how gossip spreads even without flames to fan it. And from what little I know of the anti-clerical movement it appears to be gaining a hold up and down the country, while these Lutherans keep coming across the Channel. "

"Certainly a wind of change is blowing. I would not wish the people under my charge to be alarmed by false reports. So I propose to call an extra Chapter meeting, tomorrow, to put right any misconceptions the brothers may have."

At ten in the morning the monks gathered in the Chapter House, as they did every day, but to their surprise the day's business did not start with an assessment of the work done the previous day. After opening in prayer the Abbot announced:

"I have something to say which may come as a surprise to most, but perhaps not all of you. I have today sent my annual report to the Father Superior at Citeaux, and it includes a matter I feel I must make you all aware of. This is not because I fear any anxiety over the matter, but because I wish you to be in possession of certain facts which may have already reached your ears in the form of inaccurate rumours. After I have spoken I will take three questions only.

You will know there is a vogue sweeping the country relating to the renegade ideas of Martinus Luther in Germany and Johannes Calvin in the Netherlands. Some call it Dissent, some Protestantism, some anticlericalism. In brief, they repudiate the 39 Articles of our faith and would have us study the Bible in its English (and in my view erroneous) translation as well as setting aside some of our ceremonies and objects of worship. They attack the reputation of our late great Cardinal Wolsey, and they reject the authority of our Holy

Father the Pope. Well, we can resist all these new ideas and preserve the sanctity of our Order.

What concerns me more is that up and down the land ordinary English folk are repeating these heresies and embracing the new learning. It is said that they hold much sway at Court. The King himself, long may he reign, is a good Catholic but he is surrounded by subverters. One such, and I have this from the mouth of one in high places, is Master Thomas Cromwell the Lord Privy Seal. Master Cromwell favours anti-Papal and Dissenting views and he has enormous influence at Court and with the judges. If there is danger to our way of life, it may come through the growth of the anti-clerical movement. It could be that great landowners such as our neighbours, and descendants of our founder, will espouse this new cause and seek to make life difficult for us in our enclosed places. It may be that novices will no longer flock readily to our Order, nor poor people wish to work for us. My brethren, we may have to meet a quiet revolution. I am sure you will all face it with steadfastness and unwavering fidelity."

For some time the brethren were silent, stunned by the Abbot's words. They sat cowled and with hands hidden in their sleeves, in the appointed order of seniority which was the custom at Chapter meetings.

Walter the Guestmaster was the first to seek permission to speak. "Reverend Father, how must we react if important visitors try to engage us in discussion on these matters ? I'm thinking that travellers from places of learning, London or Oxford, may come here evangelising."

"Indeed, Walter. I imagine you will respond with your customary courtesy but without uttering any kind of an opinion. There is no need for us be involved in controversy. Daniel, you have a question?"

"Reverend Father, is it possible we shall be asked officially to change our services, to read aloud in English or even give up our Latin studies ?"

"Have no fear, Daniel. We shall observe the Daily Office and sing our Masses as we have always done. I personally will vouch for that. If we are asked to display our objects of veneration less openly, well, I daresay we can move them without reducing our adoration. While I am in charge here the Englishman Tyndale's Bible will never replace our Catholic one, and your work of illumination, Daniel, will continue as before. One more question: Theodore?"

"Reverend Father, as you know my work as Infirmarian does bring me in contact with others outside our Order, and I must confess to having heard a little of this Anti-Clericalism. But, with respect, how much have we to fear from this Master Thomas Cromwell? Is he a power in the land?"

Godfrey did not at first reply. Looking round, he sensed an atmosphere of anxiety in the Chapter.

"I would be less than honest if I pretended to you. Master Cromwell does indeed hold a great deal of authority. As a well-educated young man he was Solicitor to the great Cardinal. He travelled widely in Europe and I suspect imbibed many of the radical ideas that were in the air in the twenties. He entered Parliament and his power steadily increased. Some three or four years ago he was appointed Master of the Rolls, then Lord Privy Seal, so that he is now the King;s chief legal adviser. Last year he brought in the Act of Restraint, which means the Bishops no longer are obliged to hand their first year's income to His Holiness. My information, on good authority, is that even now he is drafting the Act of Supremacy. If this goes through it means that the King will be our Sovereign Lord and Head of the Church in this country. Now let us turn our thoughts to the day's routine business. Brother Joseph, will you give us your report on the repairs to the refectory roof?"

And so Godfrey sent them from the Chapter meeting not very much wiser, and certainly unprepared for the events of the next few months. In this they were in much the same situation as the communities in other monasteries, scantily informed about political affairs, cocooned in the apparent security of their community, naïve in trusting that their Abbot could deal with all eventualities. Only Godfrey had some inkling of what might lie ahead.

III

SPRING 1536

Without an order from the Abbot no one may presume to give, receive or retain anything as his own, nothing at all – not a book, writing tablets or stylus – in short, not a single item, especially since monks may not have the free disposal even of their own bodies and wills. For their needs, they are to look to the father of the monastery.

The Rule of St Benedict in English, chapter 33

O n a calm spring day in 1536 the brothers of Abbey Dorsley were going about their routine tasks.

Brother Daniel in particular was deeply involved in his artwork, near to completing a page of his vellum manuscript of Psalm 127. This had taken him five months, and those who had any special knowledge of illuminating agreed it was one of the finest they had seen. In winter the scriptorium had been too cold and his hands too numb for the most intricate lettering, but now with warmer weather he was making good progress.

Beginning with an indented and multi-coloured capital N, five lines in depth, he had gone on to outline several lines of text in a simplified Gothic script. The uprights of the N were interwoven with the wings of a dove, and curlicues overlapped the bird's body. On the first capital letter of the facing page he planned to insert a hare, the symbol of the Gloucestershire countryside. He had heard that the Romans had depicted hares in the mosaics of their Cotswold villas. The curling finials of the N would enclose the outline of tiny animals, perhaps a spider or a bee. Next he would colour in the capitals, using only vegetable or mineral inks and the finest goose quill pen. He was copying a Latin Psalter borrowed from the cathedral, where there was a collection of manuscripts and even a few printed New Testaments, but introducing his own ideas and ornamental devices between the words. As a novice until a few years ago he had been well educated by the older monks, so that his grasp of Latin was better than many of his fellows.

He mixed his own pigments, preferring to rely only on his own colour judgements and adding to his stock of well-tried botanical and mineral ingredients when he needed to. The dark red of the main letters came from madder root (rubia tinctoria, he reminded himself) ground up with pestle and mortar. For a darker red he burned in a chafing dish a little ferrous earth, sienna or umber. Because these substances were not easily come by, and the parchment valuable, he was at pains to get the colours exactly right before beginning on a letter. Traces of green rocket (sysimbrium verdis) were extracted by boiling the herb; and cobalt blue derived from a carefully heated mix of sulphate, oxide and acid. His most precious paint, gold leaf, Dorsley Abbey bought in minute quantities to be hammered into a paper-thin sheet for gilding some of their altar ornaments, allowing Brother Daniel a minuscule share for his aureate artwork, here and there depicting the aureole around the head of a saint.

Brother Daniel loved this work and was oblivious to all that was going on in the Abbey when he became absorbed. Often he would linger alone in the scriptorium until it was almost dark, having to be reminded of the Daily Office. Other friendly monks would call him when the bell rang for Nones or Vespers. ("Think yourself lucky, Brother, that we do not follow the old Benedictine Rule with twice as much time spent in church. Here at Abbey Dorsley we have time to follow our own pursuits.") At the moment he was entirely preoccupied with the interstices of the N, fashioning curlicues and tendrils of

21

what might perhaps develop as a vine or some other flowering creeper, growing around the whole text. The Gothic lettering in red madder was closely compressed: *Nisi Dominus, frustra labor aedificatorum.* The lines must be large enough to read but small enough to be contained in a border of intertwined scrolls and Celtic crosses. Later he would pick out the capital letters with goldleaf and a green ink based on a mixture made from greenweed rocket and the juice of ground camomile. The lay brothers would compete to see who could find the best and most unusual pigments for him. The blue of woad, isatis tinctoria, he found a shade too strong for his manuscripts, and crushed ragwort had too short a life for his yellow designs.

Daniel's imagination ranged freely over the natural world, plants, animals , fishes, and the stylised shapes he had observed and admired in other men's work. But no one at Abbey Dorsley equalled his craftmanship or his enthusiasm. He was an original artist, expressing himself and his love of God with pen and inks. His illuminating skill he saw as a gift from God, and he offered it back to God in his prayers.

Abbot Godfrey had been known to stop moodily in his daily perambulations to consider Brother Daniel's efforts.

"And the one hundred and twenty seventh Psalm has taken you two months *so far?* It is as well we do not have a lordly patron demanding a manuscript by a given date. Suppose I were to set you a deadline, as I believe the printers call it. Would you be able to execute the commission?" Unlike some of the monks, Brother Daniel was not intimidated.

"Reverend Father, I might be able but I would be unwilling. This work cannot be hastened."

"And your eyesight? How much longer do you expect to continue?"

"As long as our Heavenly Father allows me to."

"H'm. It seems to me some part of each day could be more usefully spent. There are many manual tasks needing attention."

"Is not this a manual task I am doing for God, Father?"

Daniel was aware of the Abbot's limited artistic sensibility, and recognised that he was tolerated because his work brought some credit to an otherwise unremarkable provincial Abbey. Manuscripts illuminated by him were in the Cathedral library, and some months before he had drawn up an illuminated address to be presented to the king's uncle when he stayed a night at Abbey Dorsley. Meanwhile he was content to draw and paint and decorate the Word of God on parchment for as long as his eyesight – and the other duties imposed on him by the Abbot – allowed.

The coloured inks he needed were ground for him by lay servants, villagers who collected the necessary materials and plants and occasionally minerals dug up in rocks on the Cotswolds. Goose feather quills were supplied by Brother Leo from his small flock. The vellum, costly calfskin or kidskin, Daniel was allowed to buy from travelling salesmen who called at the Abbey from time to time. Parchment was supplied by Brother Stephen when he had stripped the fleeces he used for his weaving – after the fleeces were removed he processed the sheepskins to a special thinness for Daniel.

Brother Stephen was equally absorbed, weaving the coarse woollen cloth for the monks' habits, dyeing it a more consistent white and stitching the cloaks, tunics and cowls for winter and summer wear. He found the tailoring a satisfying occupation, and praised God that he was not obliged to work a boring black fabric, except for the scapulars worn over the shoulders for church services. The Cistercian Order had demonstrated its independence from the way of its predecessors, the Benedictines, by changing habits from black (the colour of evil, they believed) to saintly white. Saint Benedict had drawn up the Rule by which they lived; but some 400 years earlier Bernard of Clairvaux and an Englishman, Stephen Harding, had introduced at Citeaux in Burgundy the white habits, the simpler life style, the greater emphasis on manual work and silent prayer, reading and meditation. All this Stephen approved of, and he was proud to share his monastic name with one of the founders of his Order, and an Englishman at that. He was happy in his work and a contented member of the small Cotswold community, so long as he was left alone.

His task was to wash and spin the fleeces brought in heavy piles each summer by tenant farmers who grazed the Abbey lands; the soft curly fleeces, smelling strongly of sheep and somewhat oily. With dissolved fuller's earth dug up locally and mixed with water he cleansed the fleeces from their lanoline oil, and spun the tangled fibres on the spin-ning wheel made by a local wheelwright. The next task was to weave the spun yarn into thick lengths of cloth (though smooth, for this Order did not demand hair shirts) and finally to cut and stitch the woollen fabric. His loom was a much-used one handed down from earlier generations of Abbey Dorsley weavers. The habits were all different, for Brother Stephen calculated the height of each brother, and his girth round the waist. He took pleasure in tailoring the indi-vidual habits, though this would be strictly against the rules of poverty and collective obedience of the Order. Theirs was an enclosed community (though the enclosure was laxly observed at the present time) so no outsider examined their dress, except for guests staying in the guesthouse or the poor who waited each day at the gate for alms.

The monks were enjoined to put aside all material desires, yet many of the brothers were known to have secret aspirations. Daniel and Stephen quietly hoped for some worldly recognition of their particular skills, and it was rumoured that the Bishop intended to pay one of his rare visitations to the Abbey in the next few months and observe the work that went on there. The Bishop, Stephen observed, could hardly be called an unworldly man, living as he did in a palace, maintaining a large staff of servants, and a stable said to belong to one of the finest households in the west of England.

At mealtimes, when the Order ordained that they must remain silent and listen to lengthy readings from the Holy Book, several brothers were impatient to be back at their tasks; not least Leo, who longed to be outdoors with his herbs, his bees, his fish and geese.

On this warm spring day Brother Leo was happily occupied in clearing the banks of the fishponds. After a difficult winter, with harsh frosts and heavy snowfalls, it was a pleasure to clear the ponds and check that the carp had survived the winter. The ponds, a string of five or six, had been dammed up from the slow-moving stream which flowed through the Abbey grounds, meandering across the flat lands after springing up in the chalk hills. The Abbey lay at the foot of a narrow valley cut into the chalk, facing west, a setting so serene that guests wondered how the brothers could ever bear to leave such a spir-itual haven. The springing arches fashioned by skilled masons from the same local stone soared skywards, and the green of the cloister garth and Leo's garden perfectly complemented the pale stone.

Later in the day Leo would use his close mesh net to trap some of the fatter carp and take them to Brother Cuthbert for the monastery midday meal. The Abbot was especially fond of fish, and if he had guests he would order extra fish; trout were bred in a separate pond for this purpose. The fish ponds were only one of Leo's responsibilities, but an important one in view of the limited food products available at the Abbey and the number of guests the Abbot took it upon himself to entertain. The dairy would provide milk and cheese, bread came from the bakery, but supplies of vegetables, eggs, fish and fruit were entirely up to Leo. The bees were especial favourites, their honey used to sweeten certain flat rye cakes and milk dishes.

Much as he loved the herb garden, gathering herbs daily for the kitchens, and the physic garden, where he grew medicinal plants for the Infirmary, Leo's most cherished domain was the orchard. Not every Abbey had an orchard so well stocked, or a gardener so knowledgeable about grafting, cross-pollination or pruning. Leo had learnt much of his fruit wisdom from his father, a farmer who had cultivated table fruits in the Vale, and had bred some new varieties on the old English stock. The apricots grew against a south-facing wall, quinces (good for jelly) on a low wall to the east, and medlars, pippins and bullaces in orderly rows between the walls. Pears he trained in the French espalier fashion. The most secluded corner of the orchard was given over to the monks' small cemetery, the grass always closely mown. Here Leo liked to sit and contemplate the grassy mounds, each bearing a wooden cross with a name carefully carved by Brother Joseph in his carpenter's workshop. Deaths were not frequent in such a small community, so all the brethren were expected to attend each funeral in what Leo thought of as his orchard, and to sprinkle holy water and incense on the plain wood coffin.

Occasionally Abbot Godfrey would carry out an unannounced tour of inspection of his whole domain, overseeing that everything went smoothly and no brother was slacking in his duties. This he did today.

"Well, Brother Leo, how many fish shall I get for supper? A change from the endless carp would be pleasant. And perhaps some chicken broth instead of so many eggs. Is it not possible to vary our diet a little more? I hear that at Tintern they have salmon from the river, and cabbages with some real flavour. Ours too often remind me of paper."

Leo also would not be browbeaten by the Abbot.

"I daresay at Tintern they break the Rule and buy produce from the local farms, your Reverence. Here I am proud to say we are self-sufficient. You do not complain about the honey or the trout, I notice."

These three, Stephen, Daniel and Leo, were something of a trial to the Abbot but he acknowledged the Abbey would be a less successful place without their expertise. Beggars cannot be choosers – one of his pet sayings, though hardly apt for a senior churchman who lived as comfortably as he did. The brethren generally held that his bark was worse than his bite. Punishments were seldom imposed except for venial sins, such as leaving the abbey grounds without permission, and the bolder ones among them would indulge in a little gentle repartee with the Abbot, though only when the wind was in their favour. It was observed that Godfrey preferred the company of those who did not allow themselves to be cowed by the authoritarian style of their Father in God. On this particular day in 1535 the atmosphere was peaceful, the Abbey ran smoothly, and there was no hint of the horrors that lay ahead.

It was Robert, exercising the Abbot's horses (he kept a princely stable for a man of God, arguing that a prince of the Church must not be seen riding a nag or offering poor mounts to important guests) who brought news of a cavalcade of horsemen approaching from the Oxford direction. He rode into the Abbey precinct to warn the lay brothers working in the yard.

"Richly dressed men on good horses, some of them with heavy saddlebags. We had better prepare stabling and fodder for the horses. They don't look like Churchmen, more like noblemen."

Within minutes a posse of ten men arrived at the Abbey gate and knocked loudly for admittance. The leading rider spoke with authority and scant regard for courtesy. "Bring us immediately to Abbot Godfrey. We are pressed for time and about the King's business."

To the startled Abbot this man identified himself as Thomas Cromwell's secretary, Secretary Dawson, empowered to carry out a valuation of all monasteries in the west of England, and to assess their yearly income. He demanded to see all the Abbey account books and to inspect the work and worship going on. He also required the land overseer to yield up records of all the Abbey Dorsley property, fields, woodland and granges. He and his men strode through the precinct, the cloisters and the church, asking questions, commenting adversely on the Abbey's productivity and noting the apparent idleness of those brothers not actively engaged in work at the moment of scrutiny. When the brothers broke off work to attend the midday Mass of Sext, Cromwell's men continued their intrusive and noisy tour of the monastery.

After a cursory glance, Daniel's work in the scriptorium appeared not to interest them. But Brother Stephen's activities aroused a good deal of curiosity.

"These fleeces are paid for? How much a fleece? And how many habits do you make in a year? So many for so few brethren? Are none of them sold outside the Abbey? None? What of the Abbot's robes – these are not made by you? Why not? And who makes them? You can hardly be carrying out Abbot Godfrey's orders. This does not seem a very profitable exercise, Brother."

Leaving a bemused Stephen, who could not grasp what lay behind the questioning, three of the visitors descended on an unsuspecting Leo among his bee skeps.

"How many hives, and how much honey is produced in a season? The surplus is surely sold off to local people? You *give it away*? Come, come, Brother, this seems remarkably wasteful. And do you not grow more herbs and vegetables than the Abbey needs? There is a physic garden too, we note. And fish, poultry, eggs? Who buys these? All kept for the benefit of Abbot Godfrey and the monks – this is hard to believe."

Leo made indignant protests. "You must not suppose the Community is greedy.The Abbot has many guests to entertain. The lay brothers, the servants and workmen must all be fed. We give food to the poor when they ask us.

I do my best to provide what is needed, not an excess, and I regard it as my offering to God."

The response was scornful. "You will gain nothing by trying to obstruct us. We advise compliance, or it may go against you later."

After three hours of intrusive questioning and investigation – one of the party made notes of all he heard and saw – the ten men brusquely accepted food offered by the Guestmaster, ate and rode away without even the courtesy of a farewell to the Abbot.

The Prior reported at once to Godfrey. "Ill-mannered and ill-educated men with little understanding of what we stand for and what we are about. Did they explain their visit?"

Godfrey spoke cautiously. " I would prefer this not to be known to the Community. I had heard rumours – rumours only, mark you – of these new Visitations authorised by Chancellor Thomas Cromwell. Their purpose is not clear, but it may have to do with the King's financial needs and his interest in this new Protestant faith spreading here from Germany and the Low Countries. Now that he calls himself Supreme Head of the Church in England, the suspicion is that he will enforce some Lutheran practices here, and the inspections are to determine which Houses and which Orders might have restrictive regulations imposed on them. Worse still, these men are drawing up inventories to settle how much each Cistercian House has underpaid in taxes. The King remains an orthodox Catholic, but his adviser Cromwell is said to be covertly persuading the Court towards the ideas of Luther and Erasmus. They call it the New Learning. It is vital we do not accept this assessment they seem to have been carrying out, and above all that the brothers do not suspect it has been anything more than a routine Visitation. I do not intend to have our life here disrupted by this ungodly Chancellor whose motives I distrust."

"Your Reverence, what defence do we have against this new movement, the so-called New Learning. Is it possible the King will allow interference in the traditional way of life of our Order?"

Godfrey did not reply. His expression implied disquiet.

Elsewhere the rule of silence prevented the monks from openly discussing what had happened, but some whispered communication was taking place in the workshops and the scriptorium. Daniel's illuminated sheets had been thumbed, the parchment tested and notes made of the materials he was using. In the tannery Stephen had been elbowed aside and his unworked fleeces counted. Leo was perturbed that the visitors had seemed to make an inventory of his bee skeps, his fruit trees and poultry. He had heard muttered remarks to the effect that the garden produce was more than could possibly be needed for a community of 24 men. He had tried to protest that the Abbey provided hospitality for as many again in a week, but he had been rudely silenced.

Others among the brethren felt their work had been undervalued. It was as if a crowd of barbarians had trampled through the Abbey precinct, contaminating its sanctity.

An air of gloom and anxiety hung over the whole Abbey. It was not relieved by the Abbot's embargo on any discussion of what had happened. For a time there was hope they would be left alone. Three months later the thunderbolt struck.

Word reached the Abbot from neighbouring communities that an Act of Parliament had been passed decreeing not merely the restriction, but the arbitrary closure of all monasteries with a presumed annual income of less than £200, or answering to a Cromwellian charge of abuse, idleness or misconduct. Godfrey was confident that Dorsley's income exceeded £200 and instances of misconduct had not been recorded. (Other charges, such as abuse of privileges or poor discipline, could hardly be levelled against Abbey Dorsley – could they?)

Soon after this a letter reached the Abbot bearing the King's seal. It informed him curtly that Abbey Dorsley had been judged to be inefficiently run, liable to wasteful production and indiscipline. Its declared income of £300 a year was inaccurate, and the Community too small to be viable. Messengers from London would arrive within a month to supervise the decommissioning of the Abbey, the sequestration of its worldly goods and expulsion of all those living within its walls.

Abbot Godfrey summoned the brothers to the Chapter House for an extraordinary meeting of the Community. Even the old and infirm were not excused.

"My brothers in God, what I have to tell you sickens me as it will you. I shall read you the letter which has reached me from London. It has the King's authority and I cannot fight against it. It may be you will find ways to circumvent this awful ruling. In the name of God I ask you to bear the news patiently and with fortitude."

When he had read the letter there was a long and disbelieving silence. Some of the older members of the Community sobbed. Walter the Guestmaster was the first to react.

"Surely, Reverend Father, we can appeal against this monstrous injustice?"

"I fear not. A new Order in Parliament forbids all monastic appeals against anti-Papal laws."

"Heaven forbid that it should come to this, but can we leave Dorsley and throw ourselves on the mercy of another Cistercian House for shelter?"

"There may be nowhere left to hide. In any case we might endanger others also."

"This man Cromwell. Has he the authority to do this to us?"

"He is Lord Privy Seal and the King's right hand man of law."

"And what will become of us? Are we expected to go into hiding or assume disguises? Will any good Catholic families give us homes or jobs? How can we observe the daily Office without a church to worship in?"

Suddenly Anselm the Baker, unable any longer to restrain himself, burst out.

"They cannot do this to us! A God-fearing and well-conducted community for 400 years – we have done no wrong and harmed no man. They would treat us as if we were criminals!"

Questions and answers went on. For two hours the Community raged and queried the edict. Some, like Leo, were furious; others, like the gentle Infirmarian Theodore, were too distressed to speak.

Finally Godfrey closed the meeting. "My brothers, there is little we can do except pray that God will lift this burden from us, or give us the strength to bear it." The prayers of the brothers, kneeling together at Mass or in the silence of their cells, poured up from within the walls of Abbey Dorsley more earnestly than ever before.

IV

THE END OF ABBEY DORSLEY

A letter sent from Guilbert de Rougier, Prior of the Abbey of St Mary the Virgin at Dorsley in England, to the Reverend Father Joscelin of the Mother House at Citeaux in France. June 1536.

Reverend Father,

I do not know how to write this down. Terrible things have happened to our beloved Abbey and its people. False word or rumour may have reached you. In case it has not I am commanded by the survivors of our little Community to set down the facts as far as we know them. Forgive my poor way with words. Please pray for us, and if you can, in the Name of Our Lady send us help.

Seven days ago a letter reached Abbot Godfrey, God rest his soul, from London. It told us that King Henry had ordered his Chancellor, Thomas Cromwell, to oversee the closing of certain smaller monasteries in his kingdom. Previously ten noblemen had investigated our Community. They assessed its value and the merit of our work and worship. At the time there was no suggestion that Abbey Dorsley was under threat of closure, or its people at risk. We continued to observe the Daily Office, to celebrate Mass and carry out our daily tasks as we have always done.

Three days ago an army invaded our peaceful sanctuary and ransacked it. This was not a uniformed army, but a troop of horsemen led by Thomas Cromwell himself. They rode through the precinct striking any who got in their way, shouting oaths and trampling the cloister garth. Our flower gardens and vegetable plots were destroyed. They desecrated all sacred areas and finally entered the abbey church itself.

I myself did not see what happened there, but others tell me they smashed or snatched up holy objects: the altar frontal embroidered for us by the women of Dorsley; the silver Crucifix over the altar; and silver vessels used for Mass. After doing much damage they ordered the entire Community, monks, lay brothers and servants, to gather in the cloister. The man Cromwell told us without apology or explanation that we must all leave the Abbey at the end of 24 hours. There would be a count and an inspection before to make sure we all left, taking nothing with us but clothes and a small allowance of money which would be handed out to us. Those who could might find homes in the village; the others must fend for themselves or take to the road. When Father Godfrey pleaded for exemption for the old and the infirm, the man Cromwell said there could be no exceptions. 24 hours later he would return and any of us who did not present ourselves, to be searched and dismissed, risked death. Then he spoke terrible words. He said the Abbey buildings would be wholly or partly razed to the ground, either by fire or demolition.

At this point our much respected Abbot spoke out with great courage. I remember his exact words:

"Master Cromwell, if a finger is laid on any of these of God's people in my charge here, I swear I will personally avenge them. I am not a soldier, nor have I any skill in arms, but I will offer my own life for my fellow religious. I dare you to so much as touch one of them."

The rest of us were too shocked to know how to react. I heard a growing murmur of support for the Abbot. The man Cromwell regarded Father Godfrey with scorn.

I felt something must be said to save our Holy treasures, for you must know the Abbey owns some rare and valuable relics. So I spoke out, in spite of my fear:

"Master Cromwell, allow us at least to take to a place of safety some of our Holy objects."

Others called out: "What will become of us? Or our manuscripts?"

There began to be a mutter of opposition against the ungodly men. One or two, brave souls, tried to leave the gathering, and some of Cromwell's men forced them back. The disturbance grew. Then Brother Wilfrid, God forgive him, in his righteous rage struck one of Cromwell's men. He has always been somewhat rash in his reactions. A general commotion broke out. A few of our brethren were knocked to the ground, or horsewhipped. God will surely forgive our desire to protect our own, Father, for we are men of peace but driven to extreme measures by these dreadful events. We felt more powerless than I can tell you. Some of our brethren could do nothing but sit and weep. Some fled, taking with them for preservation from the infidels whatever they could lay hands on . I believe a few of our manuscripts were saved. Some of us retired to the church to pray and seek divine guidance in our hour of despair. This we did all through the night.

Now it is almost impossible for me to write down what happened at dawn next day. Some dozen of the Chancellor's men rode again violently into our midst, with swords drawn. They ordered all of us to stand at the Abbey gate. They saw that we were fewer than the day before. They had a list of names, and read them out like a roll call. Those missing were Brother Wilfrid, Brother Leo, two of the lay brothers and Robert the stable groom. One of Cromwell's men said they must be found; he would hold Abbot Godfrey personally responsible for their attendance. By midday every one of us must gather in the garth, to be counted. They would give each of us, young or old, a small amount of food and money to make our way in the outside world. Many brethren protested that most of our Community had spent their adult lives in the cloister, and so they would not

33

be capable of independent living. Our protests were brushed aside. By midday the five absentees had not returned. The rest of us had made small bundles of our few possessions, a wooden crucifix maybe, or some books. We had no clothes except our monastic habits. Cromwell's men roughly searched us for hidden valuables. The two oldest brethren were too weak to make any effort for themselves. Godfrey begged that they be allowed to remain in the Infirmary, with one servant to look after them. Very reluctantly the aggressors agreed to this.

Then Brother Daniel broke out into a great weeping lament, for which he could not be blamed. "My manuscripts and my painting tools. I cannot leave them. They are no benefit to any one but me. Dear God, please let me keep them. Please." One of Cromwell's men took a horsewhip to him, and Daniel cried out louder than ever.

Then Godfrey rose up in rage and spoke with such vehemence as I have never heard him use. " I said that if any of you desecrators dared lay a finger on my people I would offer myself instead. Take me, then. I defy you and all your petty orders. This is a house of God, where God's divine work must go on in spite of you. Leave alone my people and my abbey. Get out of here, each and every one of you. God will visit His wrath upon you."

Four men seized our Abbot and led him away, roped to a horse. His last words to me were "Guilbert, look after my people. The community must continue."

As we found later, they hanged him on the tree outside the Abbey gate, and left his wretched body there for passers-by to stare at. Some travellers stopped to pray or cross themselves, but many looked away as if they had seen nothing. Reverend Father, let all your people pray for the repose of the soul of Godfrey le Verbier, for he was a great and brave man of God.

As for the rest of us, we must live in the outside world as best we can, each for himself.

I write in sorrow and despair, Reverend Father. Pray for us all. Guilbert de Rougier.

V

HOW THEY SURVIVED

Brothers sent on a journey will ask the Community to pray for them. They ask
the prayers of all for their faults, in case they may have been caught off guard
on the way by seeing some evil thing or hearing some idle talk. No one should
presume to relate to anyone else what he saw or heard outside the monastery.

The Rule of St Benedict in English, chapter 67

It was only much later that I heard news of the fate of my fellow-religious. Most of the servants and lay brothers fled to other parts of the country. Guilbert and Walter the Guestmaster made their way back by a strange boat journey from Wales to France, from whence they came originally with our Father Abbot, may his soul rest in peace. Our good gentle Infirmarian Theodore stayed in what was left of the Abbey to look after Adam and Peter. Both of them died within a year of the tragedy.

In the case of Adam it was to be expected, but poor feeble-minded Peter never really got over the shock.

After he had buried them in the graveyard of Dorsley village church, the good Theodore set out to find some caring work where he could still observe his Catholic faith. In time he discovered a hospice for the poor in the east of England where he was made welcome and invited to serve, and his religious belief not questioned. Theodore was a holy man who deserved some joy in his old age, and I am glad he found a niche for himself.

Three of the brothers found villages with sadly neglected churches needing a parish priest. Joseph, Vincent and Stephen were accepted by various villagers, given lodgings and the opportunity to say Mass daily as well as using their talents as craftsmen in the village community. Now and then I was able to send a message to each man, and secretly their replies would reach me, an outcast, whereas they were respected members of their parishes.

It was not too difficult for our Cook and our Baker to find new homes and new occupations in some of our big country houses, though of necessity at a distance from Dorsley. I hope and believe they are among Catholic families who care for them.

Now I must record the hardships encountered by Wilfrid the Miller, Daniel our Artist-illuminator, Septimus a Novice, and Robert who had been a Novice but later became the Abbey groom. Life after the attack was not easy for them.

Wilfrid's story, as he told it much later to Leo

I knew I had to escape quickly after I struck and perhaps killed one of those evil men. There would be no mercy handed out for that. I had no plan in my head, but more or less following the sun (it was now late in the day) I headed north-west, on foot, following narrow sheep tracks. I carried my Missal and rosary, a loaf pressed on me by Brother Anselm, and a very small amount of money which Walter the Guestmaster gave me when he saw I was minded to escape. First it was necessary to slide and scramble up the escarpment the nearest way, tearing myself and my clothes on the thick scrub, in order to throw off any pursuers. On the way I found some mushrooms, to keep off hunger. I remembered seeing the ruin of a Roman villa nearby; so I headed that way to look for a spring where I could drink and clean myself up.

Strange to think there was once a noble Roman family living here (so the antiquarians tell us)as orderly a life as we do – no, used to do –

at our Abbey. I found the spring and washed quickly in case any traveller came by - there's a track below the wood which shelters the villa ruins. All you can see above ground are some crumbled walls and fragments of a coloured pavement. I've heard it said these Romans had skilled artists who painted floors and walls as cleverly as our monks paint on parchment. The antiquarians have picked up broken sherds of pottery and even coins with the heads of Roman emperors. Well, I can't dispute what they say; they tell us the Romans lived here a thousand years ago, mostly before Christianity came to Britain, and all I've heard about them was second hand from men more learned than me. I'm not much of a reader and I've no skill with words, so I look to others to smarten up my story.

It struck me there was a need for disguise, in case I was spotted. What on earth would folk make of a muddy and bedraggled monk miles from any religious house? With a jagged rock I was able to rip my habit and knot it to look like a farm worker's smock. The cowl could be taken for a peasant's hood. But my sandals and Cistercian satchel were a give-away, so I threw them into the brambles. Now I needed shoes of some sort, and a sack to carry my few belongings. Then – God is good – the problem was solved by a shepherd coming along the track, guiding his flock to graze lower down as darkness came on.

"Good friend, as you see I'm without shoes; mine wore out, and I'm forced to travel on foot as far as Wales tonight. Can you help me? Do you live near?"

I must have cut a sorry sight, for this obviously poor man was straightaway anxious to help me.

"My son, my sheephouse an't any comforts or anything useful to you. But you'm welcome to a mouthful of my bread and cheese, and this sack, if it's aught help at all." His Gloucestershire dialect was so strong I had difficulty understanding him, but it was important to let him know I wasn't merely a needy local.

"God bless and reward you, my friend. I'll be glad of the sack, but keep your food. You'll need it if you have to stay out on the hill all night with the sheep."

I gave him a few pence – nearly all I had – and hurried on across the flat heath before he could ask questions. Struggling barefoot over rough and marshy ground was no picnic, but I was determined to find a good cover before I set about turning the sackcloth into foot-coverings.

This took me until it was barely light enough to see. With what was left of my girdle and some sharp brambles I found to hand, I fashioned bags for my feet; uncomfortable but a sort of protection. Judging it to be about time for vespers, I said the Mass and my rosary for a while, and started on Anselm's loaf. This would perhaps have to last me for days.

As chance would have it, this turned out to be a moonlit night – the moon in its last quarter before the full – so after this wayside observance of the Office and a bite of food I shuffled on in my makeshift shoes, dodging any areas where there might be nocturnal travellers, till I came to a broad track. I could tell by day it carried a lot of horses and wheeled traffic: perhaps the road I had heard of, leading from Tewkesbury Abbey to our founder's castle at Berkeley. I crossed this track while the moon was behind a small cloud. I was not minded to stop until sunrise, with many miles between me and Abbey Dorsley.

With the first hint of daylight I stopped again to say the Mass (this would be about the time of Prime; sinfully I did not observe Matins or Lauds as the darkness gave me no guide as to time, and I was anxious to press on before full daylight.) As I trudged I prayed. Hunger and exertion was no problem; I am well accustomed to fasting and hard work. But I would have been glad of a map to tell where I was heading. No matter; the Lord would guide me.

With sunrise I saw to my surprise that I'd come to the banks of a wide slow-flowing river. This then must be the Severn, which on clear days we could see from the Abbey grounds as a far-off silver ribbon. And here at a guess I would be some way upstream from Berkeley, with Wales signalled by far-off hills to the west. I argued with myself whether to cross the river into Wales, though it seemed all too likely the great abbeys there would be suffering the same cruelty we'd just experienced at Abbey Dorsley. I would not face that again whatever the price.

The river was a serious obstacle, too wide to cross by swimming where I reached it. I guessed I might be twenty miles upstream from the estuary. The lowest bridge I knew was at Gloucester (where to enter the town and the abbey you must cross over seven arches and a causeway, almost certainly guarded). To reach it I would have to follow well-trodden routes where constables or king's officers might be on the lookout for me. It was likely I was a murderer, and murderer of a royal messenger. Religious houses a-plenty I knew of in the town or outside the walls, but I'd no means of knowing if they'd been dealt with the same shabby way as Abbey Dorsley, or if they might even now be quarters for king's men.

However here where I found myself there were signs of a ferryboat crossing; I might be able to reach the other bank if I could board a boat without being spotted. It's a place where they fish for eels and a few fishermen's boats were tied up at the jetty. One of the fishers was emptying his net of fish into a bucket. I remembered Our Lord's saying – 'I will make you fishers of men.'

" Dear friend and follower of Christ, will you take me across the river in return for some bread and a few pence? I have nothing else to give, and I must reach the Welsh border today."

But, unlike the kindly shepherd, this was not a fellow-Christian. He muttered some abuse: he was far too busy to row across this morning, and his boat was not for hire. He told me to wait for the ferry. The risk was too great; others were arriving, and if there was a hunt out for me these were poor people who would be glad of a reward. Who could say how far news of the sacking of the Abbey might have travelled?

Not knowing which way would be safest, I turned north along the bank of the river hoping to find more fishermen or an easier crossing place. It was still early and few people about. After a mile or so I began to see sandbanks and a narrowing of the river, where it formed an S-bend. It came to me this might be a place where I could partly wade and partly swim to the other bank. Everywhere was deserted; not even a farmer ploughing. On the far bank a small settlement, hardly even a hamlet, and beyond that friendly forest. I'm not a powerful swimmer, and I might be spotted from either bank. But it was a risk I had to take, before boats or carts were on the move.

I took off the ragged remains of my habit and knotted them round my neck, with the crude footwear and what was left of the shepherd's sack. My conscience wouldn't let me dispose of my missal, rosary or cross, so they went in the sack. The loaf of bread had been eaten. First I knelt and prayed; then I pushed through the reeds and walked up to my waist on the sandy bottom. I'd no idea how fast the current flowed hereabouts, or how deep the main channel might be – quite deep, if fishing boats were moored here. About ten feet into the river I had to swim, not easy as the sack and tunic soon weighed me down. I paddled on, feeling myself pulled downstream by the current. About halfway across exhaustion set in, and I had a real job to stay afloat.

Then I was altogether surprised to hear a shout from the far bank. I was too far gone to see who called, but not too far gone to grasp a rope thrown to me. Someone hauled me ashore, and only just in time. While I lay gasping on the bank an oldish man who looked as if he might be a scholar bent over me making concerned noises.

"You were in some danger, friend. The river hereabout is treacherous. What made you try to swim across at such an hour when there will soon be a ferry you could catch lower down?"

"Sir, I have no money and only the clothes I am wearing."

"So, a misfortunate. Where are you making for?"

This question really stumped me. Where, indeed?

"I'm hoping to reach Wales before tonight."

"So. Wales. You will find the border an unfriendly place for a man without food or money. Soldiers and bandits lurk there. How do you come to be in these dire straits?"

He seemed a goodhearted man, but one who expected a reasonable reply.

"I am a miller, but my mill was burnt down and I have to reach friends in Wales."

"Well, there's not much I can do to help you find work, but perhaps I can help you a few miles on your way. Come to my house first to dry yourself out and have a hot drink."

I dared not accept the offer, but it was tempting. Might this man have official friends?

"Sir, I must hurry if I am to reach my friends tonight. I can dry out as I walk." All this while I was struggling into the remains of my habit, and trying to keep the sack out of sight in case the stranger was curious enough to look inside it. I saw him eyeing the remains of my white habit thoughtfully.

"Very well; I will not press you to take refuge in my house against your wishes. But at least I can give you food and drink, and some money to guard against any more disasters. Follow me, and do not be too proud to refuse an offer that is kindly meant. I can see you are not willing to answer questions, so I'll ask no more."

At his house, a redbrick and thatch cottage near the river, he signalled me to wait while he fetched bread and cheese in a basket, beer in a leather bottle, and a purse with coins.

"I cannot properly thank you, sir. God bless you."

"No thanks are needed, but in case you are in trouble again you may wish to remember my name. It is Samuel Ford of Newnham and I am a lawyer in Gloucester. Now take my advice and keep to this track. It is an ancient Roman road, not much used, but you may get a lift in a wagon. If they ask where you are bound, it might do no harm to say the Abbey of Tintern. Many travellers on this track are heading in that direction, so it will be easily believed. People here do not inquire too much into the affairs of others, but if you are persecuted you may mention my name. It is well known hereabouts."

I was so overcome by his generosity I must have stammered my thanks in a clumsy fashion.

"No more thanks, Brother Miller. I wish you a safe journey towards Tintern."

I did not stay to find out if he recognised that I was a religious – could it be my rags? – or if he was storing up a memory of me to tell others. I trusted him, this man who had saved my life and provided me with necessities, but was this worldly ignorance on my part?

His advice seemed good, so I trudged on southwards, following the river bank, but dodging into the bushes if I heard voices or the hoofs of horses. The sun was up by now and I guessed it to be about seven, the time of Terce, so out with my rosary and a rather hurried Hail Mary. God would forgive me, I reckoned, this being an emer-

41

gency. A few hours further on and I stopped off the road, in a wooded clearing, for a small amount of the stranger's bread and beer – which I must make last as long as possible. It struck me that I had not slept for thirty hours or so. Next I skirted round a largish village which I thought might be Lydney. One of the lay brothers at Dorsley had talked of his home village, in the Forest of Dean, almost opposite the great castle of Berkeley. I was curious to see the castle, home of our founder who came here with William of Normandy, so I stepped aside to get closer to the riverbank – and there it was, a great grey pile some miles off on the opposite bank. A fine stronghold against enemies coming upriver, I reckoned. And this was a major mistake on my part, for I was overtaken by a group of horsemen who also paused near the river for their horses to drink. They wore the livery of some household, and their manner was not friendly.

One of these men called out to me: "You there. You look like a stranger here and hard up. Where are you from?"

I was quite ready with a story that I was a pilgrim making for Tintern Abbey, but to be asked where I was from took me by surprise.

"From over beyond Gloucester, sir."

"So why take this rough route when there's a better track over there?"

"Sir, I was anxious to see the castle. I've heard much about it."

"So. What have you heard?"

The questioning went on, and it dawned on me these men were suspicious, perhaps supposing me to be a criminal escaping from Gloucester Gaol. I felt they were sizing me up for some purpose I could only guess at. I had heard of harmless countrymen being seized as cover for a band of robbers. At last they rode off, but looking back repeatedly to see if I was following. I made my way back to the edge of the forest, avoiding the inhabited places, and then struck to the west along a track too overhung with branches and too narrow for horsemen to pursue me. I seemed to have shaken them off, but the danger was that they'd had a good look at me and would describe me to other travellers. I'd no doubt that if I was arrested and searched my connection with the recent terrible events at Abbey Dorsley would be discovered, and my life in danger.

To plunge deeper into the forest was my best hope.

I followed the path of the sun whenever I could see it through cloud and leaves. The day was warm and my wish to sleep very strong, but I felt driven to keep going more or less westwards. A strange place, this Forest of Dean, according to travellers' tales I had heard before I came to the Abbey. A place of mysteries and murders, so they said. For hundreds of years no strangers entered the Forest. It was cut off by two rivers and a wild marshy area, so that it was more like a huge island. Families worked the raw materials and farmed, their animals roaming half-wild in the clearings. The families inter-married and handed on their rights from generation to generation.

The Forest had supplied archers for the landowners' private armies, fighting when feuds cropped up between rival lords. It was said one Forest bowman had fired the arrow that killed a great rival of one of the Lords of Berkeley in a dispute about land across the Severn. They said too that this man fled back to the Forest and Lord Berkeley rewarded the man's family with land and livestock grazing which would always be theirs. Some Forest men boarded the ships built on the Severn, and made a fortune – or died – overseas. As I beat down a path between the huge oaks and chestnuts I fancied the shades of long-dead Forestmen watched me, guarding the mines and fields and quarries their ancestors worked.

Sometimes I heard voices that seemed to come from nowhere and disappear again among the giant trees. Once or twice I glimpsed a deer leaping across a ditch, or heard the calling of hounds, but there was no telling if they were after deer or wild boar. Far off a hunting horn sounded. The Forest was full of birdcalls and strange echoes, a place of secrets.

After an hour or two the dense forest began to break up. I had heard there were iron mines, and I looked about, thinking a disused mine would provide a good refuge for the night. I heard the sound of axes on timber, and smelled charcoal burning. I was careful not to let myself be seen. The sun now was hidden by cloud, and I was far from sure I wasn't travelling in a circle. Quite late in the day I stumbled into a dip in the land with the ruins of a castle and some abandoned huts. By now I was simply too much in need of sleep to walk any further. God's providence led me to a deep stony hollow, perhaps an old quarry, where I could see a dark patch of bushes. Most thankfully I crawled into what proved to be a hidden cave.

Here I slept deeply till the sun rose next day – twelve hours, I guess. The place was dry and nothing disturbed me, not man or beast, mouse or owl. Thinking back to that unbroken sleep after all my troubles, I cannot doubt the hand of God guided me there and watched over me. When I crawled out it was into another fine autumn day, but a less secluded place than I'd supposed. The hollow was larger than I'd guessed, and a huddle of men were roasting meat over a log fire not a stone's throw from my hiding place. A cheerful lot they seemed. Should I try to creep away unseen, or risk asking them my whereabouts? I took a chance.

"Good friends, I was lost in the forest last night. I'm heading for Wales. Can you point me on my way?"

Of course they were indeed startled to see a big man (I am over six feet and broad-chested) appear from nowhere and interrupt their meal. One or two made as if to leave in a hurry, but a red-faced fellow in a leather apron answered me without fear.

"Brother, we'm can see you're in a sorry state. Us'll ask no questions how you came like this, will us lads?"

He spoke like the shepherd of the day before, and yet his dialect was different and more sing-song.

The others nodded, but I could see they were nervous. What was I? Thief? Gaolbird? Escaped madman?

I felt inclined to trust them, honest-seeming men with the tools of their trade alongside; picks and shovels and heavy sacks. Their hands and faces were somewhat blackened, which puzzled me.

"Good friends, I'm alone and penniless and I'm asking only for directions. I won't stay to bother you."

There was a bit of a conference before the spokesman spoke up again.

"Well, we'm glad to oblige a man in need, ant us, lads? You'm fancy a bite of our roast lamb?"

They made signs that I should sit down with them and I was handed a meaty bone.

"You'm not asking who us be or why we'm eating in the wood?"

"Well, friends, I can see you're working men – like me – and I daresay you're just off to work?"

They laughed at this.

"Workers, yes, but we'm on our way *from* work."

"You're nightworkers, then?"

Little by little I learned about them – freeminers, they called themselves, entitled by birth and parentage to help themselves to coal from the deposits in the forest; but they usually did their mining when the commercial coalowners were not involved, mostly nights and holidays. There were six of these cheerful fellows, and it seemed they were also entitled as commoners, once in a while, to one of the sheep that roamed the unfenced forest. This now was their quarterly feast of free mutton, to be enjoyed after a hard night's work.

I asked them about the mining. The forest was dotted with surface mines, they told me, and they had an ancient right to take as much as they needed for their own families, but no more. It all went back to an Act way before their time. This was an ancient settlement, then? It had houses a hundred years old, they told me, an alehouse called the Cross Hands, and a manor house lived in by the family who owned some of the local mines – and, for good measure, some seams of iron ore. Two of the men worked at iron furnaces, making spades or locks or pitchforks, and two others were craftsmen in wood.

"Only the best wood, mind. Oak and chestnut, us saw into lengths to be sent down the river, maybe for ships or great houses."

"How does it get taken out of the forest?"

"Ah, there's one or two have mighty great waggons and they'm carting the timber to wharves on the Severn."

One more man, the spokesman for their group, told me he was a joiner, fashioning dressers and chests for families who could afford them. "And what's your line of work, brother?"

I told them my old story, and not so far from the truth: that I was a miller whose mill had burnt down, and seeking to join friends over towards Wales. They nodded at this.

After a good feed and a good chat I thanked them for their hospitality, blessed them and set out again, following the directions they had given me towards Tintern and the Welsh border. I reckoned it would be wisest to avoid the crossroads at the centre of the village, and the alehouse. The day lay ahead of me, and I began to feel less in danger and more confident of the future. That day I covered about twenty miles through the forest, following narrow paths and keeping the sun always on my left. When night came again I reached the banks of another fast-flowing river. There was the possibility of being seen from a craft on the water, or by travellers going towards the mouth of the river. So I made myself a bed of leaves under some bushes, and said a Mass to myself – a full and solemn one this time, with thanks to God for my preservation so far. Then I settled down for another night's sleep in the forest.

At dawn I set my mind to the problem of crossing this major obstacle. There seemed to be no bridge, ford or ferry. I must make my way south, and hope to find some kind of settlement where there might be fishermen or one of the timber barges the miners had told me of. After some hours of following the river bank I met some travelling tinkers carrying their pots and pans on a donkey.

"Friends, can you tell me the name of this river and how I can cross over ?"

It was difficult to understand their speech, not at all like the dialect of Gloucester, but I made out the name Wye and the town of Chepstow – the market place, they called it.

"My thanks, friends. God speed you on your way."

One of them spat, perhaps displeased at the name of God, and they left me in a hurry.

I trudged on another ten miles or so and found myself coming near a small town where, God be praised, there was a stone bridge across the river. I walked over the bridge and turned northwards. No one questioned me or tried to stop me. Northwards, then, towards (as I hoped) that famous abbey over the border in Wales that I'd often heard of. The valley here was flat and less forested; in the distance I could see hills again, reminding me of the Cotswolds. It was raining, I was ill dressed for the time of year and I'd very little prospect of a solid meal or a roof over my head for yet another night. I was much troubled wondering what had become of my Dorsley brothers. Were any still alive? I was troubled too by my conscience. I had behaved without caution, with passion, ánd who knows if I'd brought death or injury on some of my fellows. I had no means of knowing what their fate had been. I should not have fled as I did – a coward's escape. Surely God would punish me for my foolhardiness and pride.

Towards evening, as the light was fading, I rounded a bend in the river valley and saw ahead of me, through a thin veil of mist, a miraculous sight. Here were the undamaged and handsome buildings of a great religious house, far bigger than Abbey Dorsley, with cottages clustering round it: so awe-inspiring a sight in the twilight that I wondered if I was hallucinating. Not so. Faintly I heard the ringing of a bell, the Vesper bell.

By instinct I hobbled to the gates of this refuge. My feet were raw and bleeding, I was sorely hungry, exhausted and aching after seven days of almost incessant walking with little sleep or food. I no longer had the strength or the willpower to disguise who I was; it was all I could do to beg the gatekeeper for shelter.

"Reverend sir, have pity on a homeless man. I am a miller driven from his home and work. I have neither money nor worldly goods. I ask only for a night's bed, but I cannot pay."

"Sir, Christ said even as you do it unto the least of these my brethren you do it unto me. You are welcome to the Abbey of Tintern, which turns no one away."

"This is truly Tintern?"

"Indeed. Come in and rest, brother."

VI

ROBERT THE GROOM

Do not grant newcomers to the monastic life an easy entry .....If someone comes and keeps knocking at the door, and has shown himself patient in bearing his difficulty of entry, then he should be allowed to enter and stay in the guest quarters for a few days. After that he should live in the Novitiate, where the novices study, eat and sleep.

The Rule of St Benedict in English, chapter 58

I'm not at all sure I ever truly wished to be a monk. I was pledged by my parents on my sixteenth birthday. No choice, really, with an older brother in the army and one going in for law. Also my mother was dead keen to have one of us in the Church, following the model of her two sisters, both Superiors in convents. I'd no sister, so it was made clear to me from an early age that the family's hopes were fixed on me. I put up no serious opposition, I suppose, and never thought through what would be involved in entering the Church for the rest of my life.

My father was a master glover and bootmaker, two commodities highly regarded at the time, and we lived fairly comfortably in a town house in the Cornmarket, near the centre of Worcester. It's a decent walled town with a bridge over the river Severn and good views of the Malvern Hills. There's a ruined castle built by one of William the Conquerors' knights, where I and my brothers used to climb and play war games when we were little fellows. As we grew older and and learned to ride we'd take our horses across the river and way up into the hills. This was wild country, much better for war games. They say Gilbert de Clare and his wife Joanna had a ditch dug along the ridge of the hills, to mark the boundary of their land for hunting, and this greatly annoyed the bishops who reckoned the land on the hills belonged to the Church. So there was an almighty row, and the de Clares had to fill in half the ditch. (They were nothing to do with the Poor Clares who had a nunnery at Oxford. We never saw them because St Francis forbade women to preach. This always seemed unfair to me, and I suspect it did to my aunts who were sisters in the Dominican Order. Why should not women preach and teach as the friars their brothers did? St Francis was wrong about this, I fancy.)

The other thing about Malvern is the Priory, and near it a holy well. They tell you that if you drink water from St Anne's Well it can cure all manner of ills, from boils to kidney infections. We used to ride that way to watch the sick pilgrims standing in line to drink the cure. There was talk of miraculous healing, but I never saw a miracle. In Worcester too we had a hospital for sick paupers, St Oswald's Chapel. Once it was a refuge for monks with leprosy, then a common graveyard. Folk say that if the graves are ever dug up leprosy will return to Worcester. It may be true; so far none have been dug up. So one way and another Worcester and Malvern had a history of holiness, and perhaps this influenced my parents when the time came to settle my future.

But until I was sixteen I had a good deal of freedom to travel the country and stay with friends all over the Midlands.

I went to the grammar school, the King's School, where I daresay I was an average student, neither scholarly nor downright lazy. Having a good voice (so they told me) I sang Gregorian chant in the Cathedral choir, which gave me a taste for sacred music and the ceremonials of the Church of Rome. Several of my fellow scholars and fellow choristers had sisters I rather fancied, ánd I won't deny that I schemed and manoeuvred to go riding with them or to meet them at local festivals. There was one, Agnes Farrell, let's say I kissed her once or twice, and I think she didn't dislike being kissed; but her family persuaded her to take the veil, just as mine talked me into accepting the tonsure. We had a tearful farewell before she left to become a nun, and I just grew used to the idea we'd never meet again.

As well as a good voice I had a good pair of hands on a horse. Riding and hawking occupied a deal of my leisure time. We could ride out of the town through one of six gates in the town wall. Bridge Gate leads out across the river towards Malvern and Wales. Fore Gate leaves the town northwards, past St Oswald's on the way to Kidderminster. St Martin's Gate leads to Droitwich, famous all over Europe for its salt mines; and Friars Gate opens on to an establishment of the Greyfriars (the Franciscans.) Sudbury Gate goes to the south, as if you were making your way to London. Here is St Wulstan's Hospital, almshouses for elderly merchants, which some people call the Commandery. My father, being a good man, used to visit former merchants there, and I think he helped to support the Commandery.

At one time I had some idea I'd like to follow my father in his business. Worcester was well regarded all over England for its gloves, and my father one of the best glovemakers in town. It used to amuse me to wander into the workshop to look at the skins laid out for my father to choose from. The finest of all were doeskin, taken from young female deer, to grace the unstained hands of young female noblewomen. Next finest calfskin – always the animals had to be young. I was allowed to handle the less delicate skins, the kid, buckskin, cowhide and bullock leather for the strongest men's riding gauntlets. Powerful landowners bought these for hunting and hawking. Each hide had its individual smell, reminding me of the living animal. If white gloves were wanted, we left the skins out in the yard to bleach. The colours varied more than I would have thought possible, but after tanning they all darkened to that very shade: tan. They were brought to my father's place by fellmongers and tanners, and I swear you could sniff out what the men had been working on. Even now I associate tan and the smell of cows with the making of gloves. I think the tanning agents were sometimes alum or salt, sometimes bark. After they had been steeped in deep pits with tannins to toughen them, skins that were too stiff could be stretched over wood or metal benches to soften them. Once or twice I remember seeing the women of the family making up a tubful of egg yolk, fish oil and water for extra tough skins to soak in; and once – once only – they let me join in stamping on the skins in the tub. I enjoyed that.

After all that the skins were sent out for experienced cutters and stitchers to work on at home, pinning them on boards called donkeys and cutting with small sheep shears. These cottagers delivered the finished gloves back to my father's workshop, and they were paid according to the time spent on each pair. Different countries have other methods; in France I've heard they thin leather by scraping it with a knife over marble or slate, and there the tanning and bleaching might all be done in the fields.

When I was a boy it never occurred to me I'd do other than follow my father's trade. Then a new idea cropped up. Until just before I reached sixteen it had been the practice for boys to be accepted as oblates in monasteries from the age of ten, but the rules were changed about a year before my birthday. I did all the usual things that boys do – riding, fencing, rowing on the river – not sure if these would ever come my way again. There was a family row about which Order I should join. My father favoured the Benedictines, but mother won the day by pointing out that the Cistercians were more godly and yet spent less time saying elaborate Masses. I went along with this idea as I'd stayed once as a pilgrim at a Cistercian house in the neighbouring county, and I liked the setting and the way it was organised.

When the day came for me to enter Abbey Dorsley my mother and father escorted me to the Abbey, a ride of 40 miles or so. First we followed the river to Evesham market town, where the Abbey was founded by such great men as Kendred of Mercia and our own Bishop Ecgwine of Worcester. Abbot Clement lately embellished the abbey with a tall stone tower carrying a bell and a clock. This tower is rather strange, standing all by itself in the abbey grounds. We stopped there for refreshment, then across country a short way to Stanton at the foot of the Cotswold escarpment, a gentle village all built in honey-coloured stone. My mother took a fancy to it and asked my father if he could buy her a cottage there. I remember his reply now:

"Great heavens, Alice, do you think I'm made of money?"

"Well, Arthur, the gloves have made us rich. I should like to think you'll leave something to posterity that will last and be useful for generations."

To which my father merely grunted. He is devoted to her, but a cautious man too. Then we rode on over the high Wolds along the Salt Way. I've been told it was the Romans who first extracted the salt at Droitwich, and marked out a road for it to be brought south. This was the same road pilgrims trod in the opposite direction, journeying to the great abbeys. We crossed the high and lonely wolds for miles until we turned southwards between the famous abbey of Hailes, where the Holy Blood is kept, and the royal castle of Sudeley, now (as we saw to our surprise) shockingly neglected. Sudeley lies just above the town of Winchcombe, where two kings of Mercia are buried in the abbey. And here lives my father's brother Henry Woodward, who is a clothier with big flocks of sheep running on the Cotswold hills. We stopped briefly to pay our respects to my uncle and aunt, who gave me presents to mark my entry into the Cistercian order.

Then we pressed on towards Abbey Dorsley, climbing up on to the Cotswold Hills again and bypassing the city of Gloucester. Dorsley lies about midway between Hailes and Glastonbury, as far as I could judge, at the foot of a narrow valley running down towards the Roman Fosse Way. This is a well made road which leads eventually to the old Roman town of Bath (Aquae Sulis, they used to call it, the town of the healing water.)

We looked down on the Abbey laid out below us like pieces on a chessboard, and I wondered if all my life would be spent there. I'd have been very sad if I couldn't carry on riding and looking after horses, so I was hoping the Abbot might need help in his stables. I could see a dozen grey stone buildings clustered in a grassy landscape, with the church and its tower to the west. A chain of fishponds made a circle round the main structures. Some way across the fields there were barns and granges, and sheep grazing everywhere; but this was no surprise as I knew most of the Abbey's income came from wool. Also in the distance I could see a water mill and orchards. All in all it looked an exceedingly peaceful and a prosperous place.

After a few weeks I felt pretty much at home. They appointed an older monk, Joseph, to look after me and induct me in the ways of the Order. He was the community's carpenter, doing woodwork and repairs for the Abbey and some of its tenants, so they let me walk outside the precinct with him when he went out to work; but most of the time I helped him in his workshop. I liked that place. I liked the smell of new-sawn wood from the timber mill, and the smooth feel of the wood when Joseph turned it with adze and plane. What he was best at was repairing chairs or beds, making new legs, and re-seating the rush chairs. Once he let me help him make a prie dieu. He chose dark walnut wood, carving in one piece the kneeler, the prayerbook-rest and the back, with some decoration – leaves, I think – around the bookrest. Then we stained and polished the prie-dieu till it gleamed and looked a thing of value.

I was fond of Brother Joseph (what an apt name for a carpenter: I guess he chose it when he entered the Order) and he offered to be my sponsor when I took my vows.

This was a strange business. After six weeks the Abbot sent for me, catechised me with some tricky questions to test my knowledge of Scriptures and the Benedictine Rule. I'd learnt the Rule by heart, and I could recite certain parts of the 73 chapters set to be read throughout the year. He asked if my Christian faith was true and sincere, if I would be prepared to do any task set me by the Order, even one that did not please me. I must also agree to have no personal possessions except my clothing and religious books. Would I also observe without question those Cistercian rules of poverty and obedience? I noticed that he did not mention chastity, though this is held by the outside world to be a primary requirement for all the brethren. Not much choice: we didn't see a female from one year's end to the other, unless one or two rode past the Abbey gate in some nobleman's entourage. No female ever stayed in the Guesthouse. I presume my answers were satisfactory: I would be initiated as a Novice of the Order on St Bartholomew's Day, the 24th of August, and from thenceforward I would be Brother Bartholomew.

The ceremonies lasted all day. First my parents came to say farewell; this is not a fully enclosed Order, but they let you know that brethren are expected to leave the Abbey only in special circumstances, and to have very few visitors, unless on special occasions such as illness or a Mass of Thanksgiving on one's name day. They watched me receive my white habit, with cowl and long sleeves, and the routine sandals which we all wear. Then came the tonsuring, carried out by Brother Isaac, the deputy Infirmarian, who is also the community's barber. Of course I could not see myself with shaven head, but others told me I was almost unrecognisable from tousle-headed Robert. After this we all processed solemnly to the church, where two of us (my partner was Edmund from Hereford) were presented to the Abbot, made our solemn declarations, and repeated our vows after the Abbot and kissed his hand. Thus we became Cistercian novices, and truth to tell there had been so much novelty, new friends and new experience, I hadn't had time for doubts. Looking back on it all now I can see it wasn't really the scene for me, but at the time I felt carried along by all the persuasive ritual and the example of the other brethren. I was only sixteen and I hardly knew my own mind.

Edmund did put a question to me one day when we were walking in the cloister garth, after Terce and before our first work period. This is a quiet time when we were told to meditate, but they'd have had a job detecting us: we learned to talk in whispers, hardly moving a muscle of our faces. "Bartholomew, do you ever wonder why we are here?"

"Because our parents decided for us."

"And do you wish they had not?"

"No. What else would I do with my life?"

54

"What would you have chosen to do if your parents had not decided for you?"

"Who knows. Perhaps I would be a maker of gloves, like my father. Or perhaps not. What would you do?"

"Oh, I am content here. Most of the time."

And so Edmund sowed a seed of doubt in my mind.

After that things went less well.

To begin with I was disciplined once or twice for, so they said, cheekiness. I answered back when Brother Guilbert, the Prior, said I was inattentive to the reading at meals. I said, truthfully, that it was difficult to listen to Brother Stephen because he mumbled and stuttered over his extract from St Paul's Letter to the Hebrews. Another time Walter the Guestmaster rebuked me for not speaking civilly to a messenger from the Bishop who rode up to the woodworking shop asking rudely about some work the Bishop had commissioned from Brother Joseph. To which I said "Civility is not a one-way traffic."

Disciplining could mean saying one hundred Hail Marys, or fasting for a day on bread and water, or being isolated from the community for a day or more, in the Infirmary. All rather tedious punishments, and not likely to make me remorseful.

Then came the business of the cider. Brother Leo had made two flagons of cider from his new season's crop of apples, and by special dispensation he was allowed to hand it round himself at supper. There was more than enough for everyone, so Edmund and I smuggled some up to the dorter after Compline, and we had a few swigs after dark. For this we were reported to the Prior, who gave us a most formidable lecture and pronounced that we should be forbidden all drink except water for a month. I couldn't myself see that we had done anything terribly wrong; all the brethren praised Leo's cider, and we were not at great pains to hide our extra mugfuls.

One way and another I suppose my reputation in the Abbey was in rags. So it was no great surprise when I was told my Noviciate had been withdrawn, but that I would be allowed to continue as a lay servant, working in the stables. Halellujah! Joy! It was off with Brother

Bartholomew, that pious chap, and back to my own name of Robert Woodward. Horses had always been a delight, and helping to look after them would be more pleasure than punishment. My only regret was that the Abbot would write to my parents and they would be deeply disappointed in me. In my heart of hearts I knew the Church was not really my vocation, and I found it hard to accept its disciplines. Lay servants were seen as inferior members of the community, given few privileges, but provided with board and lodging and expected to observe the practices of the Order. At first I did not object.

A year or so went by. I enjoyed my work as a groom, and made new friends among the Lay brothers and lay servants. I was still able to see Edmund from time to time, ánd also Brother Joseph who remained my mentor and a good friend. And more and more I spent time in the garden or the orchard helping Brother Leo. No objection was raised to this, provided I did not neglect my other obligations. I think they felt he would be a good influence on me, and as it happened he greatly needed help as his gardening work expanded. I found I had a knack for collecting the bees when they swarmed, or finding eggs laid in outlandish places. When necessary I could dig or weed or plant seeds as well as the next man, in between caring for the Abbot's horses or those of Abbey guests. Nothing prepared me for the way my life, indeed all our lives, would change so dramatically.

Then came those terrible days of autumn 1536.

The first I knew of it was when I was out on the wolds exercising one of the Abbot's horses, Conqueror, and had a second horse, Black Knight, on the leading rein. Over the brow of the hill towards me came a posse of well dressed men, not fully armed but carrying swords. They shouted me out of their way with ill-mannered oaths, frightening the young horse and using their whips.

"Is this the road for Abbey Dorsley, boy?"

That "boy" angered me. I was dressed partly in monastic garb, and I was now a man.

"It may be. You might find out if you ride more slowly and make less noise."

"Impudence. Out of our way, boy."

They stopped to consult a map, and this gave me the chance to take a little-used track and approach the abbey from the north, bypassing the obvious route so that I could warn the community.

A few minutes later the cavalcade arrived and charged through the precinct, demanding to see Abbot Godfrey; on the King's business, they shouted. I was shocked at their bullying manner and lack of dignity. It seemed best to keep well out of their way, so once I had shut the horses in their stalls I went in search of Brother Leo. He was with his bees, as usual.

"You're in a hurry, my friend."

"So would you be, Brother, if you'd seen these swaggering horsemen who've just turned up from nowhere."

"Horsemen? Not anyone you've seen before?"

"No, nor care to see again, King's business or not."

I told Leo what little I knew, and I could see he was shocked too.

"Describe them to me., my friend."

"Powerful looking men, six of them, richly dressed and carrying swords. Documents bulging in their saddle bags. Men who live the good life."

"Not good news for the Abbey, I suspect."

We stayed well out of sight in the orchards, and in their trampling through the Abbey grounds the visitors overlooked us. They left after an hour or two, and we joined the rest of the Community at Vespers. There was much discussion about the whole business; only next day, when the Abbot called a Chapter meeting, did we learn more. Of course as a lapsed Brother, so to speak, I was not summoned to the meeting, but Leo and Joseph told me all. It was obvious to anyone with half a brain that this was not the last we'd hear of Thomas Cromwell's men.

Word circulated among the Community that the King's men were gathering information with a view to closing down monasteries that were thought to be less than loyal to the new protesting regime – Protestant or anti-Catholic, they called our enemies. I'm not politically minded myself, but it seemed the King was out to suppress any pockets of strong Catholicism the Lord Chancellor's men sniffed out. And Abbey Dorsley might be on the list.

For a day or two there was no news, and the Abbot spread the word that we had escaped the purging that was happening up and down the country. Leo observed to me:

"It's difficult to see what they could have against us. No religious fanatics here, no anti-monarchists; we run an orderly house, not too extravagant and small beer compared to some of the great houses."

"But the Abbot is said to have met secretly with others to plot ways and means of avoiding the ban on paying income to His Holiness."

"Rumours, my friend. Abbot Godfrey is too wise an old owl to be caught plotting."

"So we're safe from intervention?"

"Probably, unless they've heard complaints against us from landowners, or the King's men have accepted bribes to shut down Abbey Dorsley and hand over its estates to friends of the King."

"Can they legally do that?"

"My lad, with this king anything is possible."

A few quiet weeks perhaps lulled us into a sense of false security. Until the day when two dozen armed men rode up the gatehouse at daybreak and demanded entrance. It was the time between Prime and the first Mass of the day, with its elaborate plainsong, when most of the Brothers were washing the sleep from their eyes. For the rest of us, some were already at work – the kitchen staff and those going out to the fields. I recall I was feeding the horses, due to be exercised after we broke our fast at seven o'clock. It was a fine September day, with a hint of frosts to come in the air, and a light mist in the valley.

The armed men knocked impatiently and threatened to break the gate down if they were not given instant admittance. Two of the lay brothers let them in, having no authority not to do so. The Cistercian Order charges us always to give hospitality to travellers and to succour the poor and needy at the gate. I do wonder if this includes armed intruders, but this was no time for quibbling. I did not see what happened next, but I believe the brothers were ordered into the cloister – some of them half-dressed – and warned that if any tried to escape they would be taken prisoner.

Those who offered no resistance would be treated well and allowed to leave the Abbey in due course, provided with a small amount of money and provisions for the day. Within twenty-four hours Dorsley would be stripped of its valuables, ransacked and perhaps burned.

The shock affected the brothers in different ways. For some of the old and feeble it was more than they could handle; one or two of them broke down in tears.

Abbot Godfrey put up a bold resistance. He spoke of sacrilege, vandalism and crimes against God. He thundered his rage at the brutalism of the intruders. They shouted him down and dragged him away at the end of a rope. One or two others made a show of defiance: they were bound too, and left trussed like poultry in the garth.

Seeing that the same fate was likely to be meted out to us, the lay community waited quietly in the precinct. But I am not one to hold my tongue.

"Vandals ! Desecraters of this sacred place! Infidels!"

When I saw them after me, I ran by devious ways to the orchard, hoping to find Brother Leo there and warn him. I was too late. Two horsemen were flogging him under his own fruit trees. This shocked me more than anything, to see this good and gentle man being thrashed for no reason. Seeing I could not help him, I called out that I would look for him at dusk at the sluice: this was a private place of ours, where the trout were kept from going downstream by a mesh of cords. Then I went back by a roundabout way to halter Conqueror and Black Knight and ride them to safety. Fortunately for me the horsemen were too busy hacking at the gates, robbing the church and smashing the glass in the Abbot's House to notice me riding out of the stable yard. I cantered to the woods at the head of the valley – I knew every track and bridleway – and hid until it was nearly dark.

When I made my way back to the Abbey much of the woodwork was in flames: it seemed they might put the whole Abbey to the torch. By the light of this huge bonfire I found Leo tied to a tree in the orchard, where they'd simply left him. His body was a mass of weals and he was in agony. Riding Conqueror, I lifted him across Black Knight's saddle and headed us both southwards, away from the dreadful sight of the burning Abbey. Leo begged me to leave him and look after myself, but this I would not do. I made for a nobleman's estate I knew of, about twenty miles to the south, where I believed some of the farmworkers might shelter us for a short while. They were friends I had made on hawking excursions with the Abbot, who was in the habit of stopping at this place for refreshments and to water his falcons.

It was clear to me that until his injuries healed Leo would not be fit to ride; whereas I needed to be far away if I was not to be taken with the Abbot's fine horses. I handed Leo over to the care of a dairyman, Humphrey, and his wife Joan, who would look after him and hide him until he was fit to travel. I'd met them both once or twice, and I trusted them: good honest Catholics who would count it an honour to care for an ill-treated monk. Promising to return for Leo when the fracas over Abbey Dorsley had died down, I rode through the night on Conqueror, followed by a son of Humphrey on Black Knight, till we reached the safety of a farm in Somerset owned by distant relatives of my mother. I told them a much-reduced version of what had happened, just enough to win their sympathy, and urged them not to let my parents know my whereabouts, but merely to get a message to them by a roundabout route to let them know that I was safe. Humphrey's son rode home next day on a broken-down hack provided by my relatives. We thought it unlikely he would be questioned even if Abbey enemies spotted him. Then I went into hiding, with the horses (which I knew were desirable targets for any horsethief) in a derelict barn on my kinsman's estate. There was fodder for the horses, and food was brought to me secretly at an arranged place each evening. In the same way money reached me sent by my father to a village near Bath, where he had well-to-do gloving clients. So the first week went by.

My next thought was to find somewhere safer for Leo, where he could stay longterm. I was young enough to live rough or do odd jobs wherever I could, but Leo needed security and something akin to his way of life at the Abbey. Riding around the countryside south of Bristol, thinking perhaps I might eventually smuggle on board a ship at the docks, I happened to be drinking in an alehouse with two stonemasons who told me, along with other local gossip, they were about to start work building a big hunting lodge somewhere between Gloucester and Bath .

"A new lodge? Would there be a job for someone unskilled like me?"

"Sure, if you're willing to dirty your hands. A man called Poyntz has been given some land by the king for a big hunting park. He's made a fortune in spices, and he means to build the grandest hunting lodge in the west. There do be plenty of work for fit strong fellows."

They gave me directions and I rode over there a few days later, having visited Leo in the meanwhile to keep him in the picture. Masons and joiners and gardeners were already at work, and I could see this Master Poyntz was sparing no guineas to get himself a mighty fine monument. I hitched up Conqueror and strolled over to chat with the masons I'd met in Bristol. Two things I learned that shook me a good deal. The stone being brought by the cartload was from the demolished ruins of Abbey Dorsley, gifted to this Poyntz by the king himself.

The second shock was that beehives, tools and outdoor gear had been lifted wholesale from the Abbey gardens to be used for the gardens of this grand new lodge. It was as if Brother Leo himself had been robbed.

"Is this Poyntz intending to live here, then?"

"No, he's mostly at Court, being one of the King's favourites, but every few months he'll bring parties of high-ups down from London to watch the deer coursing and join in feasts here. This'll be his country place."

"So no one will live here much of the time?"

"Oh, we daresay there'll need to be folk to look after the house and garden and keep everything in good order for when his lordship chooses to turn up." The fellow I was talking to spat expressively.

"And this Poyntz has a family?"

"Only a wife, we hear, a bit of a fussy madam."

"So he'll be needing grooms and gardeners and so forth?"

"Who knows? But you could ask his chamberlain Fenton when comes to inspect the work. He's down here once a month or so."

I lent a hand with the unloading of stone and tools, seeming interested, and I rode back to Humphrey's cottage with some ideas circling round in my head. Leo listened uneasily.

"Brother, there's work there for both of us if we keep our heads down and tell them nothing about ourselves. Our story could be that you and I lost our jobs on a big estate up Worcestershire way – we won't say where – when the old nobleman died and his pushy grandson took over. You were too old and I was too independent to fit in with his schemes. But we could be useful to this man Poyntz if he's starting an estate from scratch. Little by little we'll suggest how a nobleman's hunting stables ought to be run, and we'll turn his garden into somewhere special, so that he'll be proud to show the place off to his friends from Court. What d'you think?"

"Robert my friend, how can I keep up my devotions and hide my monkish ways from these fine people? I've been too long a religious to change my ways now."

"It's not a problem. I'll persuade them you're a skilled experienced gardener, but a solitary man. You choose to live like a hermit and have your own little hut in the garden. Remember it's all a blank sheet. If we make ourselves really useful enough it's my guess they won't ask too many questions."

"And the horses?"

"I'll keep them hidden until the time's right. We'll fix beehives and a fishpond and tools for you. We'll get the man Poyntz's steward to buy fruit trees and plants for a show garden. Brother, you can keep up your own lifestyle and say Mass at all the right times – no one will know."

Leo took some persuading, but Humphrey's son backed me up (he was doing some carpentry work for the new stables) and in time Leo had to admit he could suggest nothing better for himself. We would take new names, he and I; Leonard and Rodney, uncle and nephew, and we'd present ourselves as suppliants at the new lodge, asking for work. The suppliant bit appealed to Leo; he was a true man of God, and humble by nature.

62

So gradually we got ourselves on the labour force of the estate – the Deer Park, they were calling it – and moved at first into a tumble-down cottage a mile or so from where the new building was taking shape. I planned to move nearer the stables once I'd proved my worth as a groom, and I'd help Leo to build his hidden hermitage, maybe in a cave at the foot of the escarpment. He need have little contact with his employers, and I'd do most of the talking. As for Black Knight and Conqueror, all in good time, I'd offer them as hunters bought at market for my masters. It suited us both well, for a start. In the long term I had other plans.

VII

WILFRID THE MILLER

If there are artisans in the monastery they are to practise their craft with all humility, but only with the Abbot's permission. If one of them becomes puffed up by his skilfulness in his craft, and feels that he is conferring something on the monastery he is to be removed from practising his craft and not allowed to resume it unless, after manifesting his humility, he is so ordered by the Abbot.

The Rule of St Benedict in English, chapter 57

As far as the Abbot was concerned, Brother Wilfrid was "of a choleric disposition"; to his colleagues he was a man with a sense of humour who spoke his mind; and he was permanently popular with the locals who came to grind their corn into flour at the Abbey mill. He had been known to ask for only minimal payment if the villagers were in financial difficulty, if there had been a death in the family (as happened all too often in these times of little doctoring and less medicine) or the harvest was poor. In general families brought their corn once a week and paid for the flour by weight. Wilfrid's benevolent personality cheered them and made the journey to the mill something of a treat.

His own background was modest: the third son of a miller who had picked up a little schooling here and there, and aspired for a higher status in life for his son. One of Alfred's sons would inherit the mill from his father, the second would farm the land adjoining the mill, neglected for some years because the ground was marshy and the yield poor. Alfred saw a potential in Wilfrid to achieve more in life than labouring on the land. He applied for the boy to join a religious community when he was thirteen, to master reading and writing, but also to be taught a trade. He was told that in the special circumstances of his usefulness to the Community they would take his son without the usual apprenticeship fee. Nothing was said about a vocation.

At Dorsley Abbey they offered both to educate Wilfrid and to train him in time to take the place of the ageing Abbey miller. This was not at all what Wilfrid aspired to, but he saw it would ease the family's financial burdens and might lead to better things. Best of all, it might help him to become a scholar; something he dimly venerated without knowing what it involved or how it might benefit him.

By the time he was sixteen Wilfrid could read, write, do written calculations, read the Bible aloud with some theatricality, and do a good job at the Mill. It was operated by a water wheel powered by the small stream which ran through the Abbey grounds, yielding enough power to grind twenty hundredweights of wheat or barley a day. Half of this went to the Abbey bakehouse (for bread was the staple food of the monks) and half supplied local people who came from as far as five miles around. Observing the Rule of poverty, Wilfrid could keep no money for himself, but must hand it all over to the Sub-Prior, who acted as the Abbey's treasurer. Some barley was sent to the nearest brewery, and came back in the form of flagons of very good beer, the main drink in the refectory. On one famous occasion the beer was accidentally brewed at twenty per cent proof rather than ten per cent, and half Gloucestershire heard about the tipsy monks at Dorsley. Wilfrid had too good a head to be affected by it, but he was one of few in the Community who did not stagger from the table.

Wilfrid was rumoured to have had a spell of thieving as a boy, and to be somewhat light-fingered; but he was careful not to let any of the brothers find evidence of this. He was a burly young man, rather ruddy-faced, with plenty of self-confidence and a pleasing manner.

Wilfrid's account of himself

My father was a miller and his father before him, all in a small village near the headwaters of the Thames. They said there were five mills there at Domesday, grown to seven by my time, and each one reckoned to be worth about £200 in a good year. I didn't see much future in waiting around till my grandfather died and I could be apprenticed to my father, but I knew a good deal about milling from watching them when I was a youngster. Our family mill had been restored a few times, so that we had a good building on three floors. The ground floor faced on to the fast-flowing river which pushed the paddles of our big waterwheel. The waterwheel in turn pushed two smaller wheels operating a shaft up to the floor above. On this floor stood the grain hopper over the grinding vat. Folk came to have their sacks of corn pulled up on a hoist, sackload by sackload, till they fell into the vat (the sacks, not the people, you follow?) Then an upper and a lower grindstone crushed the grain, and out it came at the bottom as flour or meal, into more sacks. My father boasted he could turn out a hundred sacks of corn a day.

As a boy I had a lot of fun climbing ladders to the upper floors, and when my father wasn't looking I would sometimes drop a mouse or a shrew into the sacks. There were always small animals scrounging food around the mill, and I reckoned they deserved a few mouthfuls. I didn't wait to see the villagers' faces when they found a live rodent in their meal. They'd pay my father so many pence a hundredweight, and cart the flour away on waggons. Sometimes they paid him in kind, with chickens or fish. We were quite a big family, so the extras came in handy.

The millstones wore out eventually, and we had to pay maybe fifty shillings for a new one cut in one of the Oxfordshie quarries and carted to our village. Our grist mill served most of the locals for about two miles around. I've heard say some landlords fined locals for taking their corn to be ground more cheaply elsewhere, but they were cutting off their noses to spite their faces; my father would refuse to grind for them if they came back in a lean year.

Of course we had problems in a dry summer when the river ran shallow and forced the wheel to turn too slowly. But on the whole good summers were balanced by poor summers. We had a millpond so that water could be controlled through a sluice at the right level; this way there wasn't much wasted water. I won't say it was an exciting life, but it was a fairly easy one.

When the time came I didn't object to joining the Dorsley community, and I got on well with most of the brothers and learned a lot from the old miller, Brother Hugh. It seemed as though I might take his place when he was too old to carry on. There was plenty of time for studying and walking on the hills. I got to know that part of the country well. They called me Dusty Miller, of course, and I daresay I was covered in flour most of the time; but I hadn't a lot to complain of, and if once in a while I thought about freedom, or having a pretty woman, well, we were all in the same boat.

I became an oblate, a kind of unofficial monk. The best times were in chapel, with music to make you dream, and at the refectory, listening to good works and the stories of the saints of God. I wondered, if I'd lived in different times, how I would have faced up to real dangers or temptations.

On that terrible day in September 1536 the first Wilfrid knew of the violent intrusion was Stephen running from the weaving shop shouting to him:

"In the name of God, Wilfrid, come at once. The Abbey has been broken into by armed men and they are flogging and tying up some of the brethren. No one knows who they are; we are all in danger of our lives !"

Wilfrid came hotfoot, up to his elbows in flour, swearing ungodly oaths. He and Stephen were quite without fear, angry and anxious to protect their weaker colleagues. In the garth they found a huddle of brothers and lay people who had been driven out, it seemed, from the church, the chapter house and the cloister. They turned to Wilfrid as one of the boldest members of the Community.

"May the dear Lord save and help us all ! Men are sacking the church, seizing all the relics and holy objects. Some of them are bundling the illuminated manuscripts into sacks. They are ransacking the Abbot's house, and we were all told to bring our habits and books and gather here. Who are these men? What will happen next? Deus miserere nos, deus nobiscum !"

Wilfrid wasted no time. He tied his habit at the waist and charged, bull-like, into the fray.

"Infidels! God will punish you for this barbarous act. You defile God's house. Put down those things which are God's. Take your hands off the old men and the boys. God Himself will judge you!"

The intruders were deterred only momentarily by this alarming apparition bellowing at them.One on foot threatened Wilfrid with his sword; a horseman galloped full tilt at him and nearly rode him down.

A growing pile of the Abbey's treasures accumulated on the grass. Food and drink were consumed right in front of the Community. Manuscripts were stuffed in saddlebags, and precious books added to the pile. The horsemen exchanged oaths and coarse jokes. Among the dazed community there was some wailing, while others followed Wilfrid's lead in trying to reclaim stolen objects and cursing the vandals.

Into this pandemonium appeared an extraordinary sight: Abbot Godfrey, holding above his head the great silver cross that stood on the altar, and the reliquary holding Our Lady's veil. He strode into the confused crowd like an avenging angel, and spoke with the voice of doom.

"Be warned, evil men. You bring on yourselves eternal damnation and the judgment of God. I care not if your orders are from the Chancellor or from King Henry himself. What you are doing is blasphemous and your punishment will be swift and terrible –"

Even while he was speaking two men seized his arms, gagged his mouth and bound him with rope. The Abbot made one last attempt to strike at them with the great Cross before he was pinioned.

Wilfrid and two others struggled to rescue him, but they were immediately overpowered. With his great strength Wilfrid fought back, shouting oaths at his attackers, and managed to drag himself free, knocking one of the horsemen violently to the ground as he escaped from the cloister. He outran the pursuing horsemen and the last the others saw of him was beyond the Abbey gatehouse, dodging through a side gate and along a path that twisted steeply up the escarpment.

Guilt went with him. Many times in the weeks ahead he questioned his failure to stand and fight. Why had he so feebly allowed the brutes to bind and gag his Father in God? What had possessed him, the strongest of the brothers, to flee like a frightened fool? Was it possible he had killed one of the barbarians? For the rest of his life Wilfrid would carry the burden of guilt, unassuageable by prayer or confession. But his immediate impulse, his only thought, was to escape from the horrors taking place in the Abbey precinct.

VIII

HILDEGARDE OF ELY

The aim is to provide ghostly counsel for three religious women (anchoresses) who after a period of living within a nunnery dedicate themselves to a secluded life outside ... this throws much light on life within the anchorhold, and their sundry diffucluties, whether of a domestic or spiritual kind ... . The writer's remarks reveal the sweetness and light which dwelt within his soul.

Introduction to *Ancren Riwle* (a rule for anchoresses),
attributed to Richard Poore, *c.* 1220

Sister Hildegarde applied herself with unusual vigour to the scrub-bing of the altar steps.It was not a task she had imagined carrying out for Our Lady, but the convent rules were unambiguous: every task must be shared equally among the community members, and the more unattractive the task, the more virtue attached to it. She gazed up at the Sanctuary light, at the gilded paintings above the altar, and the stained glass higher still. These were symbols of her vocation, pointers towards an unimaginable after-life. Hildegarde's wavering faith was sustained, she told herself, by these outward and visible reminders of Christianity, rather than by the music, the liturgy or the Scriptures she heard many times a day, ringing through the stone arches and passageways of this bleak building erected some six hundred years earlier to the glory of God.

This day was dedicated to St Hildegard Abbess of Bingen, a saint who had visions and founded religious communities of women in the twelfth century. Sister Hildegarde was well aware of the significance of the day, and the part she must play in it to perpetuate the story of her name-saint. Each September 17 it was her duty and (as the Mother Superior never stopped reminding her) her privilege to read from the Life of Abbess Hildegard in the refectory, to pray at Mass for her name-saint, and to make her contribution to the huge tapestry the nuns were weaving in memory of their religious fore-bears. Her religious name had been chosen for her without consultation, in the hope that she would follow in the Abbess's footsteps and so find inspiration to serve God as poet, composer and mystic. But religious verse and music roused no spark in her, and she certainly so far had not seen visions or heard voices.

On this day of all days in the year Sister Hildegarde prayed for greater devotion. She was acutely conscious of her shortcomings and lack of faith. Some of her fellow nuns exhibited rather ostentatiously the outward and visible signs of extreme piety; if it occurred to her at times that these signs lacked absolute sincerity, she thrust the thought away from her. Hers was not a vocation. Far from being called by God, her parents had used all their persuasive arts to convince her this was the right choice for her, as a third daughter and one they could not easily afford a dowry for. At first she resisted, pleading love of the outdoor life and deprecating the dowry that would have to be found for her as a Bride of Christ. But parental pressure was too strong, and the pleadings of a pious aunt who had entered a convent at the age of sixteen and – as it were – never looked back, tilted the balance.

Every day she remembered the Abbess of Bingen, that faraway German town, in her prayers. She was quite unable to call up any physical image of the German countryside around Mainz, the forested valley of the river Main, the terrace where the indefatigable nun had caused her abbey to be built. Still less could she visualise the remarkable woman who had transported her small community of Benedictine nuns there in the twelfth century. Was she tall or short, pale like Sister

Agatha or pink-cheeked like Sister Dorcas? The lesser Hildegarde longed for a portrait of her namesake, that she could kneel and pray to, but they told her none existed. She had read a Latin life of Hildegard till she knew it virtually by heart: how she had been taught by a recluse, the Blessed Jutta, who lived in a hermitage alongside the abbey of Diessenberg; how the hermitage had become a nunnery, presided over first by Jutta and then by Hildegard when she was only 38. How in time she began to write down her divine revelations in her *Scivias* – the knowledge of the ways of God, approved and blessed by Pope Eugenius III. Eugenius also exhorted Hildegard to found a convent in a place she had seen in her visions, which turned out to be an unremarkable deserted low hill near Bingen. So there she decamped with 50 nuns, and set about building a worthy shrine to her Lord.

Sister Hildegarde did her best to imagine the new buildings, said to have running water and many conveniences. To entertain the sisters the Blessed Hildegard had composed hymns, canticles and anthems; she wrote a sacred cantata (the Ordo Virtutum) and some 50 homilies to be read in the refectory. On top of all this her name-saint was a compulsive letter-writer, rebuking all and sundry – including bishops – lecturing in other towns and passing on divine warnings and prophecies received in her visions. Some called her an impostor, but Hildegarde's fellow nuns at Ely held her in as much reverence as they did Dame Julian of Norwich, their own local poet and prophetess. What could they not achieve with these powerful women of God as role models ? Thus Hildegarde meditated as she scrubbed.

My dear Lord, let the godly example of Abbess Hildegard in Germany, and the exquisite writings of Dame Julian of Norwich, guide me towards a true vocation. Let the accumulated centuries of prayer and praise in this place work their miracles upon me. Lord, help me to see the error of my ways and thoughts. Grant me obedience and humility. Take away my doubts and rebelliousness. So, on her saint's day, Hildegarde blamed herself, prayed and scrubbed.

Rumour had lately reached the Convent of the Immaculate Conception that some nunneries elsewhere in England had been closed down by the bishops because of the vanity which had infiltrated them. There were whispers of elegant dressing, lapdogs kept as pets, and even (scarcely breathe this) impropriety with visiting priests. Some Prioresses were reputed to live lives of luxury rivalling those of the bishops. Mother Superior Priscilla would have none of it. This was scurrilous gossip, put about by those who wished to discredit the Church, and should be ignored at all costs. She had conference with other Abbesses and Prioresses, and she could confidently discount all this tittle-tattle. No breath of slander should hover over her house. In particular she abhorred the idea of her girls being associated with the impieties of St Radegund's Nunnery near Cambridge, which forty years earlier had been closed down by the bishop on account of the "negligence, improvidence and dissolute disposition of its religious women." No Visitation would uncover impropriety under her roof. Not for nothing was Priscilla the descendant of a Knight Templar.

When Sister Hildegarde was ordered to leave her altar cleaning and go to the Abbess in her sanctum, she at first supposed it was to be reprimanded for some dereliction of duty. She dried her hands, smoothed down her work habit, genuflected to the altar and set off through the carved west doorway of the chapel, down the cold stone passages and across the cloister garth towards the Abbess's residence. Here she rang a bell and was admitted by an elderly nun whose vocation was, and had been for 20 years, to serve the Abbess. To be summoned personally before Mother Superior Priscilla during the working period between the offices of Terce and Sext was disconcerting. She knelt in silence, as the Rule directed, and waited. Mother Priscilla was a stately disciplinarian, but not unaware of the human frailty of her fellow-religious. She rustled a paper she held open in front of her, and hesitated before she spoke.

"Sister, it is not the custom here for letters from your family to be shown to you except perhaps in the case of serious illness or death. After much thought I am making an exception because here is news which might affect you harshly if you were still in the world. I must ask you to read this letter from your mother in confidence and not to discuss it with any member of the community. You must leave it with me, and after due reflection you may come back to tell me your thoughts."

She waved Hildegarde to a chair – in itself an astonishing gesture – and handed her the letter.

Anne Farrell had written:

"Dearest Sister Hildegarde – I wish I could call you daughter Agnes, but I am not allowed to. I am writing because terrible things have happened which you may not have heard about, and because your father has left home to travel to France. He and other devoted Catholics feel it is not safe to stay here in the light of recent happenings. At the king's command certain religious houses have been attacked or closed down, and the communities fled. As you know, your father has always been a generous patron to some of our local abbeys, and all those associated with them are reckoned to be in great danger. The king has declared himself above the authority of His Holiness the Pope, and it is rumoured he will create a new Church of England, made up of Protesters. Your cousin Reginald has fled to Wales from the Abbey at Pershore, and we hear that Abbey Dorsley has been stripped and several of the religious there killed. We believe one of these may be Robert Woodward, the glover's son. It is difficult to find out the truth, or to know what best to do. I feel we are all in danger of our lives, and I wish you might come home to be with me and with those of our family who remain. Please ask permission at least to visit us, Agnes, for we fear the worst. Pray for us all, as we pray always for you, dearest daughter.

Your devoted mother, Anne Farrell."

"Reverend Mother, what must I do?"
"Sister, it is for you to decide where your duty lies. I cannot choose for you. Pray to Our Lady for guidance."
"Are these terrible reports true? Have my father and others in fact fled because of what I am reading here?"
"It is possible. I have only hearsay, not direct evidence."
"Is there no help for these tragic communities? Can our Holy Father not intercede for them?"
"My information, such as it is, tells me the King will have his way and will close down all the religious houses which do not obey and change their rituals. He demands their total submission."

"Are the convents in danger too?"

"We are all in the wise hand of God, Sister."

"Advise me, Reverend Mother. May I at least visit my family and do what I can to help them?"

"I would not forbid this. But I ask you to return here within seven days, and not to discuss with the Sisters where you are going, or why. I am anxious you do not spread alarm or distress. I will arrange an escort for you the day after tomorrow. Meanwhile I trust you to observe your name day with as much attention as if this letter had not reached you. You may go now to your cell, and remain there till Evensong."

Hildegarde sat alone in her small white cell as daylight faded. Beside her a bed, a prie dieu, some books. On the wall a crucifix and a manuscript copy of the Rule of St Benedict. The coldness and discomfort she equated with holiness; in order to observe the Rule fully one must suffer. Until now Agnes (at times when she was alone she spoke her given name aloud, to remind herself of who she had been) had accepted the impositions of the convent without question. Now, shocked by her mother's letter, she felt both anxiety and indecision.

Dear God, How can You let these monstrous things happen? How can the faithful keep the faith in the face of such violence? I pray for the safety of my father, and of all good believers now at risk of their lives. I pray for my own family in such fearful times. Dear Lord, let it not be true that Robert my childhood friend has died. If it is true, may his soul and the souls of all faithful departed rest in peace. O Lord, hear my prayer and let my cry come unto You. Have mercy upon us and grant us safety.

A reading from the Book of the Blessed Abbess Hildegard of Bingen, Virgin and Visionary, on this her feast day, read by Sister Hildegarde of the Nunnery at Ely on the seventeenth day of September in the year of Our Lord 1536.

Brothers and Sisters in Christ, hear what I have seen and learned through God's mercy and divine instruction. Sacred music is the message of God to His people, a symbol of the harmony which helps man to build a bridge of harmony between this world and the world to come. Those who forbid singing in God's honour will not deserve to hear the glorious choir of heavenly angels promised to us in the Revelation of St John the Divine. Music brings man closer to God and his heavenly angels. God's blessing comes to us through sacred music.

Her name day, which should have been one of rejoicing and cele-bration, seemed endless to Agnes. After a feverish and sleepless night she put on travelling clothes at dawn – long before the first Mass of the day at seven – and joined the groom who was to ride with her on the long journey across country to her family home near Worcester. Their only refreshment before they set out was a glass of milk and a bun of sourdough; they were given thin wine and a loaf to carry with them. She would have wished to thank Mother Priscilla and ask her blessing for the journey, but this was not allowed. Her exeat was to be unobserved and unofficial.

The road from Ely to Huntingdon was flat but poorly marked, hard to make out in places. Then came a difficult stretch, swampy at times, from Godmanchester south west to Bedford, and so on in the afternoon towards Banbury and the Cotswolds. Now a landscape that Agnes knew better, from her girlhood excursions across the Cotswolds, hilly but well signposted. Then a twisty road following the northern edge of the Cotswolds to the familiar walls and abbey gateway at Evesham; and here a Farrell family servant was waiting to greet her and escort her on a fresh horse for the last twenty miles. Darkness fell before they reached home, but there was a slight moon and the horses kept up a brisk trot. Towards midnight Agnes fell exhausted into her mother's arms. The 130 miles on rough unmade tracks had taken eighteen hours.

The Farrell household was in distress and confusion. There had been no word from Agnes's father or her brother Edward. News from Evesham and Pershore was not good; both abbeys had been threatened with closure if they did not hand over all their treasures to the King's men and put a stop to all divine services. Travellers coming south from other religious houses had urged Anne Farrell

and her household to flee into Wales, where the anti-Catholic movement was said to be less strong.

Anne was in two minds whether to take this advice or to wait stoi-
cally for whatever lay ahead.

She had lived here at Hill Place for 27 years, all her married life.
Bertram had brought her here to his family home as a very young
bride. She looked back with affection to the first years when it had
seemed to be always summer under the giant beech trees, with a
great chorus of birdsong at all times of day and vivid sunrises and
sunsets. The house dated from the reign of Henry the Seventh, a
solid stone manor with ornamental windows and chimneys. Here in
quick succession Joanna, Edward, Patience and Agnes were born,
playing happily on the terrace as toddlers, climbing trees in the park
when they were a little older, graduating to ponies as teenagers.
Anne had loved being a young mother and watching her two older
daughters choose husbands from neighbouring Catholic families.
They lived within a day's ride now, visiting her often and bringing
their own children for her approval. Edward followed his father into
land management, part farmer, part timber merchant, still living at
Hill Place but disappearing from time to time on enterprises she did
not inquire about: she believed Bertram and Edward were in touch
with other landowners who fervently supported the Catholic cause
and were concerned for the future of the great abbeys at Evesham
and Pershore, and the smaller priory at Malvern.

Her own greatest anxiety was for Agnes, presented to the nuns of
Ely when she was only 15. There was prestige and pride in giving a
daughter to God, but loneliness also and a constant aching sense of
loss. The Order allowed parents to visit the Convent once a year.
Then she was entitled to speak to Agnes through a grille, and to walk
briefly in the cloister garth with her. Knowing that Agnes was
growing up far outside her control, becoming a woman without any
mother-daughter contact, living a life she could only guess at: all this
Anne found hard to bear.

When Bertram and Edward fled, telling her only that they had
reason to suppose their lives were in danger, not indicating their
destination so that she could not pass on information, Anne was

overwhelmed with a longing to see Agnes, if only for a day. Must she be cut off from all contact with her?

Joanna and Patience urged caution. She might be flying from one crisis to another, and unwise to alarm Agnes with the news. Better to wait for a message from her husband or son. Anne alone made the decision to write to Agnes. "We are her family. She should know of our troubles, so that she can intercede for us." The letter was taken by an old family servant who could be trusted not to talk, to deliver it into the hands of the Abbess. Two days passed without a reply; the servant was given no message. Anne waited in a confusion of thoughts, uncertain whether she had acted foolishly. Each day she applied herself to an embroidery task – an altar frontal for the local church – but this did nothing to soothe her anxiety.

"Suppose something terrible has happened to your father. How would I know? What then would he wish me to do? Should we not stop here in case he or Edward should come back suddenly and need a hiding place, or medical attention? How then would I be judged if I had simply run away?"

"Mother, look forward in hope rather than dread. Sooner or later we will hear news of them, and this will guide us in what action to take. Not all the abbeys have been closed down. They will surely have found sanctuary."

"How could a message reach us if they are in hiding already? Any messenger would be intercepted."

"Mother, you are too pessimistic. They left in good time – they had careful plans. Believe me, you will hear very soon."

"And why have I not heard from Agnes? I doubt if my letter has reached Ely, or she would surely have replied."

Three days dragged by without news of any kind. Joanna left to return to her children, twenty miles away. Patience promised to return as soon as news filtered through, whether good or bad. Anne had to acknowledge that her daughters' duties lay with their families, and that she must endure the uncertainty alone. Her relief when Agnes arrived was beyond words; here was comfort and companionship that only the youngest sister, the favourite daughter, could give her.

"Mother, I promised Mother Priscilla I would stay only seven days. She was generous in allowing me to come – I must respect her goodwill. Let me make inquiries among our friends, to see if they can suggest where father and Edward may be. It would be unwise to try to get in touch, but at least we may find out which way they rode. I also would be glad to hear news of Robert Woodward?"

At first Anne shook her head, concentrating on providing food and a fire for Agnes in her old room. "Must you wear that ugly habit even here, where no one can see you?"

"The servants can see me, and I would bring the Convent into disrepute. Gossip travels fast. I'm sorry, mother, but I must observe the Rule as I do at Ely."

"You must do what is right, and I'm wrong to try to distract you. We will sit and read the Scriptures together."

Agnes kissed her mother long and lovingly. "I do know how you are suffering – believe me, I do. But I must ask again – have you heard anything of Robert Woodward?"

Anne spoke reluctantly. "They say some of the monks and lay brothers died at Abbey Dorsley. Of course it is only hearsay, but no one has mentioned Robert as a survivor."

On the sixth day without news Agnes wrote to her Mother Superior.

"Most Reverend Mother in God,

I have prayed long and earnestly seeking God's guidance. I am conscious of your kindness in allowing me to be at this time of great emergency with my family. I am aware I am unworthy of your trust. But this is a time of crisis for all God's people, and most especially his devoted lay servants among whom I count my father, my brother and others we know. It may be they are no longer alive. We do not know the fate of those driven out of the monasteries. At Ely we have not been in physical danger, so it is difficult for us at the Convent to share the unhappiness of these men and their families. For my mother it is an agonising time of waiting for news which may be heartbreaking when it comes. Religious houses in this part of England have been sacked, burned and destroyed, and good men cruelly put to death. After receiving Communion and many prayers to Our Lady I have decided I must stay here with my mother, who is alone and needs me. We have no idea what has become of my father or my brother (we fear the worst) and my sisters are needed by their own families.

Forgive me, Reverend Mother, for breaking my vows. I pray also to our Heavenly Father to forgive me. I am making this choice with great reluctance, and in full awareness of my mortal sin. May God bless you and all my fellows in the Convent.

Your loving and sorrowful daughter in God,

Hildegarde."

On the eighth day Agnes Farrell removed her nun's habit, put on riding gear and set out for Worcester to visit the Woodward family, seeking news or words of advice for her mother.

As she reached the glover's house she was unrecognised, for none of the Woodward family remembered a young woman in a plain black riding habit with a shaven head and and no jewellery. She asked to see Dame Alice, handing over a letter from her mother, and was shown into a parlour older and more austere than the Farrell family's.

Alice Woodward held the letter and peeered shortsightedly at Agnes. "You cannot be Anne Farrell's youngest daughter? I think she entered a convent?"

"I am truly Sister Hildegarde, Dame Alice. I am here on my mother's behalf and I have forsaken the veil, at least for a time, to be with her. You are alone too?"

"Forsaken the veil? That is a bold step. I hope you will not regret it. I remember you as Agnes – you used to ride and go hawking with my son Robert."

"Indeed I did. And now I am here to ask if you have any news at all, even the smallest rumour, of what has happened to my father, my brother Edward or your son Robert."

Much guarded discussion finally revealed that word had reached the Woodwards, through secret messengers, that Robert had escaped the slaughter at Abbey Dorsley and was believed to be in hiding somewhere in the south of England. They had communicated with him by way of relatives at Bath. "But we must all be circumspect. They are in great danger, the survivors from Dorsley."

"I am so thankful for Robert and for you. But is there any word of my family?"

Robert's mother shook her head. "Believe me, Agnes – may I call you Agnes, or must it be Sister Hildegarde? – believe me, if we can hear anything of Bertram Farrell or Edward Farrell you will be the very first to know.

We have heard that good Catholic men are travelling to Wales, to Ireland, even France. Please tell your dear mother that I am sure no news is good news. I would be glad to see her again."

"I shall tell her, and while she is alone I would be thankful if you could come over to Hill Place and spend a little time with her. It would be a great comfort to her."

So the arrangements were made. Agnes sat down to meat and wine with Robert's mother before riding home. "I thank you for the offer of a bed, but my place I think is with my mother: she is both anxious and lonely, and not in good health. She does truly need me."

That same night Agnes wrote again to Mother Priscilla, confirming her decision to set aside the veil. She wrote a letter from her mother to Bertram and Edward, ("By hand of messenger, most urgent") to be delivered if there was any means of contacting them; and she wrote as an old family friend to Robert Woodward, through the good offices of Dame Alice, hoping to learn of his welfare and his whereabouts.

Two weeks passed before a letter reached her by a devious route, written by a stranger, suggesting that she make a discreet journey to a place called Deer Park, north of Bath, and ask for a garden worker named Leo, who would bring her definite news about her father and brothers. The decision to do so was a heavy one for Agnes, so recently a cloistered nun, knowing that her mother would not approve of such a risky venture and indeed had counselled her against it. The odds were against her learning anything useful, and for a woman to travel across country unescorted would be virtual folly.

But for Agnes the pain of not knowing, and the frustration of doing nothing, outweighed the risks. She prepared for the journey by kitting herself out in plain old clothes, to make herself less attractive to a highway robber, and strapping to her saddle only the most basic food and drink. To placate her mother she took with her the elderly servant, John, who had met her on the road from Ely. Her route was longer but not unlike the way taken by Robert when he first set out for Abbey Dorsley, and she had waved him goodbye on a hopeful spring day. But now it was almost winter, grey and forbidding, and England a more lawless place than it had been five years earlier. The tracks across the wold seemed far bleaker than when she had ridden them as a girl, on her way to hunting or hawking, enjoying life to the full.

To add to her doubts she was beginning to regret having left the cloister, a place of familiar security, setting off into the unknown. The future was unpredictable, the chances of making contact with the rest of her family slender. Her mother's farewell words rang in her ears:

"Remember, dear girl, that I fear I have lost a husband and two sons. To lose you too would be more than I could bear. Please come safely back to me, Agnes, and come soon."

IX

DANIEL THE ARTIST

The story of Daniel the illustrator, as told much later to Leo

At first I simply did not know which way to turn. Everything seemed hopeless. The Abbot dead, several of the brothers fled, others in a state of total despair. One or two of my unfinished manuscripts I had hidden in the folds of my habit; the rest I assumed had been burned, along with several crucifixes and carved wooden icons. It was best not to think about them. It was as if a thunderbolt had struck Abbey Dorsley, and everything I knew and loved had been wiped out.

When evening came there were only half a dozen of us left. Cromwell's men rode away, their saddlebags loaded with food, money and treasures. They left us nothing of the smallest use or value; no silver plate, no statues, no candlesticks, no censers, no holy water stoups. Abbey Dorsley, my home, no longer existed.

Then Septimus appeared. He found me sitting on the steps of the high altar among the rubble and charred wood. I suppose I was in a state of shock. "Come on, Daniel, this is not a good place to be now. Cromwell's men may come back. Others will come looting and

83

beating us up. You and I must find somewhere safe to hide for a few days at least, till the uproar dies down."

At that time I did not really know Septimus. He was a novice who had not been at Dorsley long. He sometimes came to watch me working on the vellum, or helped me mix the pigments. He was younger than me, I judged, and he spoke like a highly educated man and also, or so I thought, one used to giving orders.

"A safe place? Is there anywhere safe within miles of here? And how can we escape without money or horses?"

"Have faith, brother. What has happened is terrible beyond belief, but I have a feeling everything is not lost if we go now. Come quickly and quietly so that no one hears us. Don't stop to collect anything. Just follow me."

He spoke with such authority that I felt compelled to obey, though he was only a novice and I a Cistercian of five years' standing. So we walked fast and without speaking through beechwoods, along a narrow track leading east along the ridge, till Dorsley was several miles behind us. Once I looked back, but I could see nothing where 24 hours earlier there had been a cluster of handsome buildings with many lights piercing the darkness, offering a refuge to weary travellers overtaken by darkness. This place had been my home for six years, and my studio. This had been my inspiration and the *locus genii* for all my work, my offerings to God. I could not imagine living in any other way.

"Brother Daniel, you once told me you knew of a monastery not too far off where they have a library of illuminated manuscripts and they might know about your work?"

"Perhaps you mean Malmesbury?"

"Well, I know a man who lives in the town of Malmesbury, and I think we might get there tonight if we walk without stopping. He would give us a roof over our heads for a night or two. Are you willing to try? Good. Then I have some more news for you."

Septimus astonished me. He had a map, which we could just make out by the light of a watery half moon. In his robe he had bread and a small flask of beer. And he knew the route exactly.

Cautiously we crossed over the Ermin Way ("this is an old Roman road that runs from Gloucester to Oxford and on to London; we don't want to be stopped by the devil's horsemen") and later over a drovers' way ("We'd look like fish out of water if they saw us here; it's mainly used for taking cattle to market Salisbury or Winchester way") and kept going by moonlight south across open country, seeing only sheep and an occasional shepherd.

After about two hours' walking across rough Cotswold country, following sheep tracks and at times another drover's track, we stopped briefly to rest and eat. We met no one except shepherds and a solitary horseman, certainly no sign of pursuit or search. Now the land was sloping downhill, away from the high Wolds into a terrain of small streams which Septimus said fed in time into the Thames. I was astonished at his local knowledge.

"Now another surprise for you , Brother Daniel."

He reached again into the folds of his robe and handed me some rolls of parchment. When I opened them, I recognised some of my own artwork; not my best, but good enough to show to others. "These I think may be our passport to safety or at least temporary shelter. Now don't look so down-in-the-mouth. Admit I've made some good plans, have I not?"

I was bemused and overwhelmed by Septimus's practical help, as well as his generosity and forethought. For the first time since Cromwell's men had burst into the cloister, I began to feel some glimmer of hope.

We walked for most of that night and next morning, putting maybe forty miles between us and Dorsley, first across open high Wolds, leaving the Severn Vale behind us and avoiding any well-used tracks. I had no idea of time, except from the sun, but I stopped every so often to say the Office or say my rosary. I felt some guilt at neglecting my monastic duties, but Septimus told me positively that in the present circumstances the Lord would rate self-preservation more highly than religious observance, and who was I to argue.

Presently we dropped down into another river valley, a smaller river running directly to the Thames, Septimus said, and followed it south-west for a while through green fields and small woods.

"How on earth do you know this country so well, Septimus?"

"I used to ride with my father; he was land agent for several abbeys and kept an eye on their flocks and herds."

"So was it a false estimate when the king's men said Dorsley made more than £300 in a year?"

"Oh, very likely. I didn't concern myself with the economy; I was more interested in sketching buildings and landscapes."

"So you too are an artist!"

"I wouldn't say that. It's just a hobby."

"Did your father persuade you to enter the novitiate at Dorsley?"

"He died last year. I joined the Cistercians to please my mother."

Septimus answered brusquely and walked ahead of me, seemingly to cut short more questions.

At about midday we sighted a small town standing like an island between two narrow rivers, inside ruined walls but with a definite gateway on our side, the north side. Septimus told me some scholars reckoned it had been founded by a Scot called Maidulph, and so called Maidulphsbury. Standing on high ground inside the walls we could see a great religious building, apparently undamaged, like a galleon sailing through the meadows.

"The Benedictine abbey of Malmesbury, Daniel. Take a good look while it still stands., for I suspect its days are numbered. There's a story that nuns lived here before the Benedictines came, but they misbehaved, so it was closed down until the Normans came and built this spectacular place. King Athelstan, the great Alfred's grandson, is buried here. Some of the monastic buildings are used as weavers' houses. This is a well-off town. They say it turns out three thousand bales of cloth a year, and there's a great cloth fair on the feast of their patron saint, St Aldhelm."

"Tell me about him."

"He was abbot of Malmesbury about eight hundred years ago, and he was by way of being an architect. He designed some of what you can see now, and he wrote Latin poems and riddles."

"*Riddles?*"

"Oh yes, the people of Wessex in Alfred's time loved them. They had riddles about beekeeping, wild animals, soldiers, riddles against accidents and illnesses, almost anything you can think of. One I've heard was about a hoard of rings not made for a bride, but waiting to be kissed by a sword."

"What's the answer?"

"Chainmail."

"Why was Aldhelm made a saint?"

"Oh, I think so many folk came to worship at his tomb they said he must have performed miracles. What's important for you is he founded a fine library here, so I'm sure they will guard your manuscripts. William of Malmesbury was a great historian in the 12th century, and he built up the library. They say he turned down the chance to be Abbot so that he could carry on as Librarian, and some would call him the father of English history. For myself I think the Venerable Bede has a better claim to that title. There couldn't be anywhere much better to stow your work away for a while. Now I know a house where we can shelter for a day or two. We'll go there after dark, so as not to be seen. These are wool merchants my father had business dealings with, and they'll tell us how to get right away from here to somewhere completely safe. But I think it will be best if you let me take all your manuscripts to the Abbey (they will remember me because of my father) for safe keeping."

Of course I raised many objections, wanting to keep my precious parchments with me. But Septimus spoke masterfully, and he assured me the monks of Malmesbury would realise the importance of my work and look after it well it until such time as I could reclaim it.

Subsequent events confirmed what he had said. The wool merchant and his wife took us in without asking questions (Septimus had gone secretly ahead and gave them some explanation which they found satisfactory.) They had a handsome town house a stone's throw from the town's market cross, and downhill from the abbey, and we slept in a cellar where none would be likely to find us. Then Septimus slipped away by a little-used passage with my parchments hidden in a woolsack. In truth I was desperate to keep them, but I remembered the ones that had been burned at Dorsley. I prayed these would survive somehow. Septimus returned with a letter from the librarian at the abbey:

"This is to attest that I will hide and keep safe the twelve scrolls written and illuminated by Brother Daniel of Dorsley and given me by Septimus Flaxman of this county, son of the late Bernard

Flaxman. I also declare that if any disaster comes to the abbey of Malmesbury I will hand the scrolls for safe keeping to a layman who will guard them with equal devotion.

Signed, Oliver,
librarian of the Abbey of Our Saviour and
Our Lady at Malmesbury."

With this I had to be content, hoping that the manuscripts would at least come to less harm than if they travelled with me into who knows what dangers. I kept reminding myself that I must trust in God, however far He tested me. Septimus, bless him, did his best to lift my depression by telling me about the abbey, which he'd glimpsed after dark.

"The locals tell a story of a monk who thought he could fly and broke his legs jumping off one of the towers. The spire was one of the tallest in England, over 400 feet, but it fell down not long ago in a storm. They're still dealing with the ruins. There was damage to the chapel of Our Lady, and the shrine of St Aldhelm. In the porch there's a carving of Our Lord on a rainbow, and St Peter with his feet damaged by vandals so that pilgrims can't kiss them. When we come back one day to get your manuscripts I'll show you all this."

On the fifth day the goodhearted wool merchant led us at daybreak to an inn where we climbed into a cart taking bales of wool to the port of Southampton. We were to act as assistant waggoners. I still think of Malmesbury with much affection. The residents of the abbey and the town were good to us, risking persecution themselves. I heard later that they were able take over that part of the abbey not ruined, to use for their own purposes. Some services were still held in the chancel, but many of the abbey outbuildings became weavers' workshops and stores. A wealthy clothier called William Stumpe bought up the workshops, and he helped the townspeople take over the chancel to be their parish church. So you could say the closing of the monastery benefited them, because they now have a parish church that's second to hardly any in England.

The plan was that at Southampton we should try to board a ship carrying cloth to France, and bringing back wine. In France, Septimus said, there was as yet no persecution of the Catholics. For they had a devout king, Charles, who ruled his land with a proper respect for the Church of Rome.

We travelled with the waggonload of cloth through the pleasant market town of Chippenham and on towards Salisbury. In the distance we could see the mighty spire, but the waggoner for reasons of his own bypassed the two towns, Old Sarum and New Salisbury. As usual Septimus knew all about them: how there had been a feud between the bishops and the castle keepers, so Bishop Richard Poore started a new town around his cathedral. One of the tombs, Septimus told me, had a Latin inscription: "If you offer help, you will receive help."

"We might do worse than adopt that as our *vade mecum*," he said.

After Salisbury came the great Benedictine Convent of Romsey, where we stopped for refreshment – not telling the lay servants who greeted us, of course, that we were monks on the run (we were dressed as wool traders.) Septimus in his clever way persuaded the Mother Superior to show us the famous Romsey Rood, a carving of Our Lord with the hand of God showing through a cloud above His head, as if to say "This is my beloved Son." It was difficult for me not to kneel in worship and so reveal my monastic background. We asked discreetly if the community did not feel threatened.

"No, my friends, for the good people of Romsey have worshipped here for many years, and now they have raised the money to buy the Abbey and use it for their own parish worship. God has been good to us here. We are only nineteen sisters, so I think we will be able to stay on and serve the townspeople." This was a teaching establishment, with boys and girls studying reading, writing and the Scriptures under the nuns. I wondered if they were also taught how to draw and illustrate the Holy Book. This seemed to me the model of what a convent should be, with a devout body of women teaching, preaching and praying. Later we heard that the Abbess and 25 nuns refused to surrender to the King's men, so they forfeited their pensions and had to disperse around the countryside wherever they could find friendly faces. I hope they fared well.

The waggoner gave a sum of money for the community, and we said goodbye to some of the friendliest fellow religious we had met on the way.

Not long after this we could see, across a flat stretch of saltmarsh, the buildings of a sizeable walled town. This was Southampton, where we hoped to escape by sea, but also feared for our lives. No one challenged us as we drove through a gateway called Bargate, over the town prison, and then slowly down the long main street towards the sea. On each side we saw handsome merchant houses (but built in timber, not like our Cotswold stone ones) and some very grand shops. This brought us to the Watergate, where we left the walled town and crossed a huge cobbled yard to the town quay. Here it was all bustle and comings and goings; I had never seen any harbour before, and the press of wheeled carts like ours, handcarts and people going about their business startled me. My years in the cloister, and since then in hiding, made all the noise and movement quite frightening. But for Septimus I suspect I might have asked to be taken back to Malmesbury with our kindly driver.

The waggoner drove quite confidently on to the town quay, where he expected to find ships bound for France. After all this was his business, and he had every right to be there. I was surprised to find so many signs all around us of France, which of course is the home country of our own Cistercian mother church at Citeaux.

There is a French Street, and a French style of castle, and a Chantree, and moored at the quay I saw ships with French names: Marie Grace de Dieu, Le Dauphin (which oddly enough is both a large fish and the title of the French king's oldest son), and the like. Septimus told me the old town of Southampton had been sacked and burned by French pirates, so the townspeople settled farther west and built New Southampton, well walled and fortified, in case of further attacks; and here was the English end of the French wine trade.

This square quay is supported, I learned, by piles driven into the marsh, and it can accommodate forty or fifty ships at one time. The harbour is guarded by a castle with dungeons and a keep, and close by is the Custom House.

Here our waggon-load of wool had to be checked and weighed; the customs men gave our driver a bill of lading to show to the ship's captain, and waved us to a rather small wooden vessel tied up at the far end of the quay: the *Seigneur Roy*.

I thought she looked a sturdy boat, well put together by the carpenters and riggers, but maybe too shallow to carry a heavy load. Not so, said Septimus.

"She's clinker built with quite a deep keel. You see those struts? They hold the barrels of wine in place and prevent them rolling about in a rough sea. Now our bales of good kersey cloth can be tied down to make up the weight for the voyage back. These ships are well built to stand up to the Channel crossing – this one might even have been made from timber in our own Forest of Dean in Gloucestershire. It has good strong canvas sails; you need not be nervous, Brother Daniel. The *Seigneur Roy* will get us to France. My friend the clothier always sends his wool aboard her."

I could see one or two other French boats being unloaded: the barrels were rolled down an oak plank and across the cobbles to waiting carts. Now Septimus and I had to set to and unload our woollen bales from the waggon on to the *Seigneur Roy;* heavy labour for me, who had never had to do manual work in my life. The master of the ship, an Englishman, directed the operation and showed us how to stow the bales most economically. Then Septimus drew him aside and I saw some money change hands.

"Master Hugh will take us as passengers and keep us hidden from port officials and any revenue men who come aboard to collect the duty on the wool and search the ship. They don't take kindly to stow-aways, he tells me, and they know how many seamen he has to crew the ship. We'll have to make ourselves useful on board, take orders from any of the crew and fend for ourselves as to food and bedding. I've told him we'll make no fuss, and if it comes to a search party we'll give ourselves up. I don't want to get him into any trouble. Are you fit enough for a sea voyage and some hard work, Brother?"

"I'll do whatever you say, Septimus, to get safely to France."

And so we signed on as extra hands on the *Seigneur Roy,* a wine carrier from Bordeaux, passing ourselves off as wool waggoners crossing to France to make sure the French gave our master a fair price for his good English cloth.

We had to wait for tide and wind to be favourable before we set sail down Southampton Water, and while we waited I fretted about the safety of my manuscripts and not being able to carry on working at them. Septimus suggested I might find some art materials in the town, but I was too scared of being asked who I was, and too uneasy in my disguise as a wool carrier. What I did was to enter a chandler's shop on the quay, a dark noisome place full of rope, tar, sailcloth and hemp, and beg a scrap of parchment and a quill pen. I said I needed to make a map, and an evil fellow with warts on his face gave them very grudgingly to me in return for coins. I gather from something he said he thought I was a French spy come to spy out the harbour defences. When I reported this to Septimus he laughed.

"No, Brother Daniel, you are too shy and nervous to be taken for a spy!"

I found an obscure corner on the quay and started to sketch the ship, the *Seigneur Roy,* giving her the most beautiful ship's lettering I could devise; but the paper and pen were ill suited to sketching, and very scratchy. Septimus found some better tools and I set about drawing the Custom House (choosing the castle would have provided evidence for the spy notion) until it was too dark to see. I would have liked to say the Office of the Day or slip into one of the churches near the quay, but Septimus said this would certainly fuel suspicion. During the night we slept as best we could against some sacks of straw behind the chandler's place. At daybreak we reported to the ship's master, who told us we would sail on the next tide, at midday. And so we set sail for France, like guilty men.

X

THE DEER PARK

The bee has three natures. One is that she is never idle .... Another is that when she flies she takes earth in her feet, so that she is not lightly over-thrown by the wind. The third is that she keeps her wings clean and bright. So righteous men that love God are never idle, for they are working, praying or thinking, or reading, or other good deeds .... . They keep their wings clean, that is they fulfil the two commandments of charity in good conscience.

The Nature of the Bee, Richard Rolle of Hampole, *c.* 1340

As I get older I find the sorrows of others concern me less, Heaven help me. But it does give me pleasure to get letters from my old friends at Abbey Dorsley, to practise my reading skills and remind myself of happier days. First I must tell of my greatest pleasure, to have Robert Woodward again as a companion. He had been in hiding in many parts of Somerset and Wiltshire, only returning to the Deer Park when he felt it was safe to do so, and intel-ligently finding himself employment as a groom for Sir Nicholas

Poyntz. He said it was in order to be near me, but I don't flatter myself that a good-looking and charming young man of 25 would feel any obligation to an ageing ex-monk living as a hermit, even less aware of the ways of the world than I had been in the cloister.

Robert arrived one spring day in 1537, eight months or so after the terrible events which had driven us from Abbey Dorsley. He offered himself as an estate worker, but his skill with horses soon became obvious and he was promoted to the Poyntz stables. He was relieved to find me still safe and reasonably well in the place of safety he had found me when we all fled from the abbey. His first concern then was for my welfare, and I am thankful to the Lord for sending me a rescuer and a comforter. For me it is sad that Robert gave up his vows and lives now completely as a non-religious, but I have to admit the monastic life was perhaps not right for him.

Winter at the Deer Park had been a hard time for me, living from hand to mouth in the cave I had opened up as a shelter for myself at the foot of the escarpment below the hunting lodge. True, members of the estate staff – the dairyman and the farm bailiff – would see that I did not starve, but at times there were only building workers on the site and the Poyntz servants, if they were not on duty in London or elsewhere. It was lucky that as a boy, helping on my father's orchards, I had learned to catch and skin a rabbit, bake a hedgehog in clay and trap pigeons – though all of them scarce in winter. I had a small supply of ale provided by the stablers, and my friend the shepherd would bring me from time to time, secretly, a loaf or half a leg of mutton.

When spring came I persuaded them to let me keep bees again, for the Poyntz table, and a few carp in a pond downhill from the escarpment. With these, as well as wild garlic and mushrooms, and the herbs and vegetables I was used to growing, I made myself useful to the household. The idea of creating a formal garden came later. So when Robert arrived and found me digging I was overjoyed to see him, and I fancy he was not a little surprised to see how I had made a rough kind of home for myself.

"Brother Leonard! I've come to keep an eye on you and earn my keep from the Poyntzes, if I can. I see the big house is taking shape. Do they live here now? How are the bees?

"Robert my son! I can't say how glad I am to see you well. Is there news of any of the other brethren? Is the Prior still living? Are they all scattered, or is there any hope of reuniting us all?"

"Hey, one question at a time, if you please – "

Robert settled beside me on the orchard grass. He brought out a leather bottle and a loaf, and told me what little he knew of the Dorsley community's fate; how some had fled overseas, some found homes and work in other religious communities, some settled down to village life. But of Daniel who did those wonderful illuminated scripts, or Wilfrid who ground the flour for our excellent bread, he had heard nothing. It was rumoured that Guilbert de Rougier and Walter Lefevre had reached France. He believed the villagers of Dorsley had built a shrine to our dear Abbot Godfrey, and pilgrims came secretly to worship there.

We had so much to say to each other, he and I, but Robert warned we must not be seen too much together for fear of arousing suspicion about our monastic background. He promised to stroll down the garden whenever he could, to help me with the bees; but I should take care not to recognise him if there were others in sight.

I had a small area for growing culinary and medicinal herbs, among the vegetables, but when Lady Poyntz saw it (on one of her very rare visits) she demanded I should turn it into a pleasure garden.

"All the best houses have a pleasure garden now, I hear. Somewhere to stroll and chat and look about, with an arbour and some statues – it must be especially attractive to the womenfolk, you understand. And not so far from the house. I leave the design to you, Father Leonardo, but next time I come I expect to see a pretty place with herbs and flowers."

It was Robert who helped me plan and lay out the new herb garden, along the same lines but grander than our physic garden at Dorsley. First we marked out two square plots, each about 15 yards by 15 yards, with two sets of alleys crossing at right angles, and a further path running right round both squares, as it might be the frame of a picture. In the middle was a round raised bed which would be for a centrepiece. The edges we planted with young slips of box and yew which Robert begged from the priest of a church some miles from here. (It is a church where they have chained a copy of Master William Tyndale's Bible in English; Robert said it would do me good to see the Scriptures in my own mother tongue, but I cannot bring myself to leave this place where I feel safe.)

In the smaller squares we are planting lavender and comfrey with its pink dangling bells, which some call knitbone. They say the Crusaders brought it back from Turkey, and I know myself that a mash of the leaves or roots will make a poultice good for setting a broken bone or helping a sprained ankle. Then we planted tansy which keeps the air fresh in infected places. At Dorsley it was sometimes chopped up in the Lent pancakes, a bitter flavour to remind us of Our Lord's suffering. There was hyssop too, which we made into an infusion against coughs, and chamomile that takes away sleeplessness. If it grows well here I may make a lawn for her ladyship. Sage, with its tall purple spikes, we planted to offer sage tea; legend has it that this will prolong life. Pennyroyal (some call it pudding grass) is one of the herbs I like best to grow, and it freshens drinking water. Monkshood we do not grow as the name troubles me: it is linked to witches and the occult, though supporters of it say as an ointment it numbs pain. We have some of the more common herbs, parsley, thyme and rosemary. All of these have their medicinal uses, and some are sweet-scented as well as having pleasing flowers. So I try to please her ladyship and to have a sprinkling of the herbs I grew at Abbey Dorsley, which remind me of Our Lord and my boyhood too.

Last time Lady Poyntz was here she instructed some of her staff to scour the gardens of other country houses to stock up her pleasure garden. I wonder if this is a form of theft, but I say nothing. Visitors tell her it may rival the herb garden at Hatfield House. I suspect Lady Poyntz would like to emulate the Countess. These same visitors have brought her cuttings of friar's balsam and angelica, the Godsend plant, named after the Archangel Michael. His saint's day is in May. when the angelica first blooms.

"Look, Father Leonardo – here is a balsam named after a famous friar," her ladyship announced. She feels she is doing me a favour, and I am pleased to have little gifts for the garden.

Even Sir Nicholas takes a look at my herbery now and then, and he promises me a stone urn to stand in the circular bed as a centrepiece.

I would rather it were a stone carving from Abbey Dorsley. Robert is helping me to make an arbour from hazelwood, where her ladyship may sit in the shade and admire the distant view out across the vale. This is to be a surprise; Robert says it will do no harm to flatter her.

In time I hope to have distinct gardens; one for the herbs that cure ills, one for the plants that can be used at the great feasts the Poyntzes plan to have, one for sweet smelling and coloured flowers to please the ladies. Our Lady the Virgin Mary is often seen in pictures sitting among lilies, violets and carnations: these stand for purity, humility and divine love, so I know there can be no sin in creating a garden of flowers. And to bless the humbler plants, I am told the Dean of Wells Cathedral has written a treatise in English on herbs.

It does give me pleasure when Lady Felicity, Lady Poyntz's god-daughter, visits from London. She loves all plants, studies them and knows their names better than I do. She will trim the roses and cut a few flowers for the big house, or a nosegay for herself. Sometimes I find her under a tree sketching flowers, and she makes a very true representation of – it might be marigolds or foxgloves. Her skill with a brush reminds me of Brother Daniel, who did those exquisite manuscripts at Dorsley. Where are they now? I fear they may no longer exist.

Lady Felicity has an innocent inquiring nature and at seventeen she is loved by everyone who meets her. I marvel that she can mix happily with the young bloods and rakes who hang around Sir Nicholas. Robert Woodward would be a fitter husband for her than any of these rakehells, but he is only a servant here. Yet I know he comes from a gentle family, his father the master glover and his mother a cultured lady. Here they know him as Robert the groom, and none must ever suspect that he was once a novice monk at doomed Abbey Dorsley.

Next the bees. I can make my own skeps from willow twigs and birch bark, but I need a colony of bees to start the honey-making. My friend the herdsman (he who brings me ale) knows a beekeeper down in the vale, and he promised to let me know when his bees swarmed. The first swarm was in May. I wish I had the hat and hood, the gloves and the smoker I had at Dorsley, but I had to make do with what Robert could borrow from the families of his fellow-grooms. When I had all I needed he put me on the back of his horse and we rode through two villages (I can tell you I was nervous in case anyone suspected where we were from) and so to a farm in the bend of a small river, not the mighty Severn which flowed past my childhood home. It was five miles or so from the Poyntzes' Deer Park. The bees had left their hive and swarmed in an old apple tree, not too high up. Robert was puzzled to see how I would manage in strange territory.

"Just keep still and don't scare them. Bees are nervous creatures."

First we looked to see if they had followed a new young queen bee; for this I put on all the protective clothing I could lay hands on and examined the colony by standing on the stirrups of Robert's horse. Then we set up a ladder against the tree. Luckily the queen was there, so I placed the straw skep under the whole swarm and shook them off into it, making sure the queen went in with them. The stragglers I enticed into the skep by smoking them from behind (I had lit some dry grass and tinder in the smoker.) Just a few needed to be brushed off the branch with a goose feather. To make sure they stayed inside I fastened a cloth over the whole skep, knotting the corners so that it would be easy to carry home. We rode back without mishap; in the darkness of the skep the bees were quiet, thinking it was night.

I had made a hive similar to the skep, but bigger, with frames to support the honeycomb. Queen bees do not sting people – only other queens – so it was fairly easy to clip her wings.

Robert asked "Why do you find it so easy to spot the queen? I can never find her."

"She's likely to be flying about all over the hive, or else hiding under a cluster of worker bees. Usually she's the biggest in the hive."

"And when you open the hive, why don't they go off and swarm again?"

"I keep them shut in for a day or two, till they feel at home. Where the new queen is, that's home. Very domestic creatures, bees."

So here we are with a new colony, and in a few weeks I shall take out the first honeycomb and present it to Lady Poyntz, if she happens to be here. Or perhaps to Lady Felicity.

Meantime it's late May and my vegetables are doing well, peas and onions, parsley, chicory and carrots. The pleasure garden is taking shape, though because it's purely decorative and not useful I'm less fond of it than the rest. Now we need some fruit trees to keep the bees happy. I loved my orchard at Dorsley, and if I know about growing anything it's fruit trees. So I shall look for the right moment to ask Sir Nicholas; I expect he knows some landowners who could spare a few slips of apple, medlar, damson or quince or even bullace. My father the fruit grower would have been glad to see me making an orchard, I fancy.

Last time Robert and I were talking to the bees, along comes Lady Felicity. I could see she and Robert already know each other, and I fancy there's a bit of unspoken communication there too.

"Brother Leo, may I please see inside the beehouse?"

"My lady, it's too dangerous. Bees will sting anyone who comes too close."

"But they don't sting you or Master Robert?"

"No, because they are used to us and we are used to handling them. You have to be an experienced beekeeper not to get stung. Better study the butterflies and see how they feed from flowers. They are beautiful, like your ladyship."

"Oho, you flatterer, Brother Leo. Do you say that to all Lady Poyntz's friends?"

"No, Lady Felicity, because they are not as lovely as you."

She likes to flirt with me, because I'm old and dull and not likely to fall for her as the young men all do.

"Robert, take Lady Felicity to the pleasure garden and show her the plants the butterflies like best."

"Brother Leo, won't you come too? I shall feel safer with you – "

The little minx; I could see she was teasing Robert, and he never took his eyes off her. So they walked away together, and I can't be sure, but I think I saw him take her hand. They are young and happy; sometimes sadness comes over me when I think I may have missed that kind of happiness. Then I say my rosary and think of Our Lord's suffering.

It was perhaps a week or so after this that Robert told me he'd heard news of Brother Septimus and Brother Daniel. They were in

France, he said, and safely settled at a great abbey not far from the sea. Would I like to send them a message, and he would try to deliver it? He had plans to cross the Channel and visit this French abbey to see if a new community could be set up from among the survivors of Dorsley. An ambitious young man, an ambitious plan.

Of course, I told him, I'd dearly like to see again some of my friends from Abbey Dorsley. But I must rest content with a few messages, and be thankful that I have a safe refuge and the where-withal to carry on some of my old pastimes. Where else now could an old monk driven out of his longtime home expect to keep bees and grow herbs, and even help to set up a garden which may one day give pleasure to others? I am content at last. The Lord be thanked who watches over me.

XI

AT THE ABBAYE
JUMIEGES, FRANCE,
MARCH 1539

*A visiting monk from far away will perhaps present himself and wish to s
tay as a guest in the monastery. If after a while he wishes to stay he should
not be refused this wish ... he should even be urged to stay, so that others
may learn from his example; because wherever we may be, we are in the
service of the same Lord.*

The Rule of St Benedict in English, chapter 61

The story of Walter Lefevre, formerly Guestmaster of Abbey Dorsley in England

Here it is truly peaceful, almost as peaceful as at Abbey Dorsley – how long ago was it? Two years? Those of us who have found refuge here offer thanks to God daily for our preservation in this tranquil place, in the land of our birth, by the great river of Normandy.

Guilbert and I had no idea where we would land on the coast of France, but we wrote to brother Cistercians at Citeaux (where both Guilbert and I had made our vows and entered the Order) and they arranged a crossing for us from Beaulieu in Hampshire, where there is a daughter-house of Citeaux. Beaulieu had been threatened, but not yet closed down, when we arrived there by horse in October last year. It is a place of calm, among forest trees that have stood since William of Normandy hunted there. We left all our possessions, fearing discovery, and wore only plain clothes, not monastic habits.

The Beaulieu brethren were shocked beyond measure to hear of the dreadful death of our good Abbot Godfrey , and they did all they could to console us and attend to our welfare. This was a task I hope I would have reciprocated if opportunity had arisen. At that time we had no news of any other Dorsley community members, and I regret to say – God forgive me – I did not feel compelled to seek their whereabouts or linger to see if any would be able to join us. I bitterly regret this now I have learned of the dangers and sufferings some of them went through. I feel shame that I did not obey our Lord's commandment to love one another as He loves us. Perhaps my faith was not strong enough, my instinct for self-preservation too strong.

On the Beaulieu river a small sailing boat was paid for by the community, to take us to France with a few of their number who were due to make a visitation to their Mother House. We were blessed with fine weather for the Channel crossing – it took three days – and all of us as it turned out were good sailors. As Prior of Dorsley Guilbert had been to and from France once a year or so, but this was my first return since my installation as Guestmaster at Dorsley.

I did feel a sense of homecoming as the French coast came into view, and I do believe I was in tears. We put in at a small harbour some distance upstream from the mouth of the river Seine. The Beaulieu men were to cross by ferry and travel on by horse towards Caen; we said farewell to them with many words of gratitude, and went on by boat along the broad meandering river till we came to a flat wooded area between two bends of the Seine.

Jumieges is a handsome and extensive monastery on a kind of peninsula projecting from the east bank, overlooked by what the natives here call a Dom, a small mountain, and shaded by stretches of woodland. Here we were met by Benedictine brothers who had been alerted to our coming and our problems. So we came in the evening of an autumn day to the Abbaye of St Peter and Our Lady (as they say, Ste Pierre et Notre Dame) the place that is to be our home for the next few years. The Benedictine community has most generously offered us sanctuary for as long as we need it.

This is a place where the very stones speak of their history. Two pinnacled grey towers rise up among a cluster of red roofs; the Abbot's house stands four square, with many windows, and trees have been planted here and there which provide shaded walks. The surrounding wooded landscape is of course a mass of green, or in autumn as now gold, bronze and copper. Abbaye Jumieges was founded nine centuries ago by the blessed Philibert for the Frankish king, Clovis, and built on a huge scale. Then came Viking raiders from the north and burnt down the abbey, even as the invaders burned and looted the resting place of the Blessed Cuthbert in England. But Jumieges rose triumphant again from the ashes, built to the glory of God by the holy Saint Chambard – our Duke William attended the consecration soon after he'd been crowned king of England. Under two great Abbots, Clement and Thierry, those mighty twin towers were raised up to the heavens. They do say the second abbey had towers 60 feet high and pillars like the forest trees. It flourished until a hundred years or so ago, when great storms damaged it. Even so ravaged, the ruins are still an inspiration. Now the Benedictines are at work restoring the damaged towers and also the cloister, a labour of love but exceedingly slow. Could we, I wonder, ever rebuild Abbey Dorsley?

Not many here speak English, but Guilbert and I have not forgotten our French, and we all have Latin in common for reading and writing. The daily Office hardly differs from our Cistercian practice, though it is more formal, with much wonderful music, and there is no pressure on us to make any contribution to the life of the community unless we choose to do so. For the time being we are left to pursue out own vocation, with time to recover from the wounds of the past year. We are blessed indeed. My first task is to gather what news I can of our fellows from Dorsley, and Guilbert is occupied drawing up a full report of the atrocities at Dorsley to be sent to our superiors at Citeaux and to the Holy Father in Rome.

We feel God calls us to keep alive the flame of faith that burned so brightly at Dorsley, and in particular to see that the name of Godfrey de Verbier, martyr, is not forgotten.

So our suffering has been minimal compared with that of some of our fellow brethren. The first to reach sanctuary here was Daniel, our gentle and talented artist.

Daniel's story, told in his own words

We sailed from Southampton, Septimus and I, on a calm tide. I was in great fear of being arrested as a spy, since strangers had watched me sketching buildings on the quay, and some had asked why we were there. French and Spanish seamen loitering at the harbour were eyed with much suspicion, and I think it was only my English countryman's way of speaking (a bit of acting I learned as a boy) that saved me. If I am to be honest, one officious citizen marched me to the harbourmaster's lodging, and I was questioned closely about my intentions. I told them I was just escorting a consignment of Cotswold wool, waiting for a shipload from France to take back to Malmesbury, my home town.

May the good Lord forgive my untruths – perhaps to save one's life a venial lie may be excused? In any case I shall say ten Hail Marys and twenty Paternosters in penance. I do sadly feel the lack of monastic discipline and others to tell me from day to day what I should do. Septimus tells me I should grow up and be my own master.

We sailed down Southampton Water early in the day, hiding among the bales of wool on deck until we were well out into the open sea. Next day a strong wind blew from the south west and Septimus became green and vomited a lot. I was less troubled by the heaving of the deck, but I was not at all interested in food. Just as well, as the crew had not catered for the two of us. Out in the open Channel, with no land in sight, I feared the little ferryboat might capsize or be boarded by looters. At night the vessel felt extremely vulnerable, but at daylight on the third day we could see the coast of France and the crew told us we were nearing the estuary of the river Seine. Good; we would land soon. I was wrong. We sailed on upstream for many miles, through a landscape sadly different from my own dear Cotswolds. If I had had materials I would have felt compelled to draw what I saw, fearing we might need landmarks to make our way back.

"Septimus, have we been kidnapped? Wherever are they taking us?"

"There's no call to be so anxious. The boat's governed by wind and tide. She'll pull ashore when it's safe to do so, and a quiet landing place will be much safer for us than a busy harbour."

"I'm uneasy. Why then did they tell us we would land at the mouth of the Seine?"

"You're a nervous chap. These fellows know their business, and we needs must trust them."

Septimus was right, as usual, and we stepped ashore on a sheltered inlet very like the coves I remember from my Devon childhood. The Beaulieu seamen produced a rough map of the land, and we gave them our blessing as they set off for home. Now came the hardest test: we were far from any town, speaking no French, and with no French money. How to find shelter or a night's resting place?

That first night we slept in the open and at daybreak started walking due south by the sun. We trudged through a landscape of small fields, orchards and woods all divided by ditches. A well watered landscape, ploughed fields and sleek brown and white cattle grazing. These cows were smaller than our English cattle, and among them some goats.

Suddenly Septimus pointed: being more observant than I am, he had spotted in the distance the tower of a village church. This we thought was the answer to prayer, so we hurried towards it. As the sun rose so did our spirits. The village was not fully awake at this hour, but the church door was open – a Gothic building, larger but not greatly different from home, dedicated to St Sulpice. I had not heard of this saint, but here was a good Catholic church where we should surely find a welcome. We found a caretaker sweeping. Neither of us spoke French, so Septimus approached the old man with a few words of English: "We come from England, and we seek sanctuary. Can you help us?"

There was no response. He simply stared, so (supposing he might be deaf) I made signs to show that we were tired and hungry. The result was unexpected.

The old man attacked us with his broom, shouting what might have been curses. We backed away, not understanding a word he said. He went on driving us from the church with the broom, till we had no choice but to retreat. He appeared to be making for what I took to be the priest's house, presumably to report that two ragged strangers speaking gibberish had invaded his church. Should we wait and explain ourselves to whoever came out? I thought we should, but Septimus said no; and since his advice was nearly always sound I did not argue. We left the village by a narrow lane in a different direction, not stopping till we were out of sight and earshot of the caretaker's church. Why, I ask myself now, were we so scared? These Frenchmen had no cause to dislike or even be suspicious of us. Could it be that we felt guilty, intruders?

The next village we reached was larger and busier. We tried asking for directions to an abbey or religious house, but as before no one spoke English. We felt foolish. Then it occurred to Septimus (he was always the one with ideas) that the church here might be more welcoming.

At the very door of the Eglise de Ste Marie des Rochers we met a middle-aged man in a cassock.

"Father, we are refugees from England seeking sanctuary in your country. Can you help us?"

"My sons, please rest yourselves in my church. What would you? Food ? Water? A place to sleep?"

His accent was atrocious but his manner kind and we could manage to understand him.

Septimus showed him our rough map and asked if there was an abbey thereabouts. "Mais oui, but it is lointain."

"Could you perhaps draw us a better map?" "Bien sur. And pendant que je dessine la carte it is necessary to eat and drink."

He called to a well dressed woman at the back of the church – did the priests here have wives, as some do in England? Or could she be his daughter?

The woman fetched wine in pewter cups and a loaf of bread, for which we thanked her with nods and hand signs. The curé (she spoke to him as monsieur le curé, and we now know this is the customary way to address a French priest) produced a very creditable sketched map and showed us the route to a place he named as l'Abbaye Jumieges, near a river. Then he blessed us, and it was all I could do not to respond as a professed religious. It seemed important not to give away our connection with the Church of Rome; he needed to believe that we were English travellers who had been cast ashore at an unknown point on the coast and were searching for people we knew in the area of Rouen – this much we were able to convey, and I honestly believe we convinced him. A good man, and trusting.

The rest of our journey was without incident, and on the evening of the second day we saw the silhouette of a great abbey outlined against the setting sun. Its giant towers took my breath away.

"Journey's end!"

"Don't raise your hopes too high, dear boy. They may not let us stay here for long."

But instead we found a welcome from the brothers – though not of our Order – and familiar faces from Dorsley, and for me ways and means of carrying on my lettering and my manuscripts.

For me it is all like a dream. After all our privations and struggles I find myself in a place where the work of illuminating texts is a supreme task, one they all value beyond measure. They have shown me a treasure normally guarded in great secrecy, an illuminated letter 500 years old, the first evidence (they say) of sacred art in Normandy. It is a letter of St Augustine, with a portrait of

107

St Peter himself (Sanctus Petrus) sitting inside a most elaborate capital A: not the sophisticated art of our own day, but such fine workmanship I can hardly believe it goes back to the tenth century. And they treasure some even older art, coins bearing the inscription of William Longsword, who was first Duke of Normandy and an ancestor of our own Duke William. And I have seen an exquisite document, a history of Normandy worked by a monk at this abbey, Guillaume Caillou. Elsewhere there is a painting of Guillaume presenting his history to William the Conqueror himself. Then too they have a Collect based on St Luke's Gospel, worked in lettering so delicate it would not disgrace some of our best calligraphers today. Truly this whole abbey is one vast art collection in progress where I, Daniel, am privileged to take part. Surely Our Lord himself guided me to this wonderful place.

There are early breviaries and Bibles and texts more beautiful than I have seen anywhere, intertwined with plants and animals and lively human figures. I told Septimus about one I especially remember. It had a note at the foot: "I transcribed this work during freezing weather. Reader, be forgiving." So you see they had a sense of humour too, these monks hundreds of years ago.

So Daniel confessed his hopes and fears to Guilbert and me, and it seemed to us it might be acceptable to him and the Jumieges brethren if he were to stay here and make his contribution to their great library. They are tolerant people, the Benedictine community, and particularly in view of what we Cistercians have suffered. The prospect seems agreeable to Brother Daniel, but his friend Septimus, having renounced the life of the cloister, is disinclined to return to it. His future lies elsewhere, almost certainly back in England. Nothing compels him to stay here.

XII

THE GIRL WHO CAME
TO THE ABBAYE

Wouldst thou know the Lord's meaning in this thing? Know it well. Love was His meaning.

Julian of Norwich, *The Revelations of Divine Love, c.* 1390

The girl came riding through the gates of the Abbaye on a cart-load of apples. She was wan and thin and melancholy, as if she had been shut away from the light for too long. Her gown was of coarse hessian and she wore a kerchief tied like a wimple over what seemed very short hair. She climbed down awkwardly from the apples and the farmer driving the cart pointed her towards the guest-house.

"Voila le hostellerie de Jumieges."

She nodded thanks and pressed a coin into his hand. When a monk approached, clearly confused at the sight of a strange and unaccompanied woman, she went on one knee and spoke in broken French.

"Reverend frere, je cherche refuge. Est-ce possible que quelques hommes anglais restent ici a l'abbaye? Je suis anglaise, et je cherche mon pere et mon frere qui sont échappé d'Angleterre a cause de la closure des maisons religieux."

The gatekeeper signalled that she should wait and returned with an older monk, stern-faced, wearing the black habit of the Benedictines.

"You come from England, ma soeur? Vous etes religieuse?"

"I was a nun, but I have renounced my vows. I am seeking my father and my brother, who may be in sanctuary here."

The Frenchman indicated a degree of dislike and disapproval.

"Madame, it is not our custom to offer hospitality to unescorted women, or to disclose the names of any who may be staying here as guests."

The girl sighed and wiped her hands wearily down her skirt.

"Sir, I do not ask for food or drink. Only to learn if any of my family are in hiding here. I have travelled far and in much discomfort because one told me some Englishmen have found refuge at Jumieges, and this abbey is well known for giving help to those who need it."

There was a long pause before the Benedictine spoke again.

"So be it. Follow me."

She followed the senior monk to a small room leading off the courtyard, as it might have been the parlour in a convent.

No one spoke, but a younger man brought her water and a bowl to wash – she was covered in dust – as well as a glass of milk and a flat cake of bread.

After an interval the older man said: "We have here brothers from England who speak both French and English. I will ask them if they have any news of your family. What is your father's name?"

"Fletcher. Bertram Fletcher, from Evesham in England. He is a good Catholic, mon pere."

After this she was left alone for some twenty minutes. Once or twice men in habits peered in at her, seemingly curious at the strange sight of an Englishwoman dressed as a French peasant. Eventually she was joined by an older monk, wearing the habit of a Cistercian, and speaking perfect English.

"My daughter, I am here to help you if you are truly from England. Your name and how you arrived here at Jumieges? I must know these matters before we can talk freely."

110

Again the girl went on her knees. "Father, I have many times said Hail Mary full of Grace in the hope of finding Englishmen who might have news of my father and brother: Bertram and Edward Fletcher from Evesham in Worcestershire. They fled the country when the closing down of the greater abbeys began. My father is a devout Catholic who publicly opposed the visitations and the sequestration of holy vessels; in the end he was advised to make his way to France, my brother with him. I do not know how they reached here, or even if they did, but I was brought by a wine merchant sailing from Poole to Le Havre. Until now I have hesitated to name them fully in case they are still in danger of their lives. My mother has had no news of them. She is sick with suffering and I promised I would not return without learning something, even if the news is bad."

"And your name, my daughter?" The Cistercian spoke gently, but she saw the trap.

" If I tell you I am Anne Fletcher, reverend father, it is close to my family name."

The Cistercian took her by the hand and led her to a chair.

"My daughter, I do not seek to pry into the secrets of others. Whatever you tell me will be as confidential as if in the confessional. There are here at Jumieges no English refugees except a handful of us who were members of the community at Abbey Dorsley, which perhaps you knew of. If you choose of your own volition to tell me what has happened to you, I may be better able to help. We will ask our French brethren to make inquiries of other religious houses where your father and brother may be known. Meanwhile I will ask if there is a house in the Abbey grounds where you can stay to recover from your journey, and a good woman to look after you. When you have rested I will visit you to hear more of your journey, and any details which may help us to trace your family. I believe what you tell me and I wish to help you, but you must understand your story is a strange one which will not necessarily be believed by others. Local people I suspect will not look kindly on a young unmarried woman travelling alone and not speaking their language. I advise you to be discreet in what you tell those who ask."

"Abbey Dorsley? You are from Abbey Dorsley, father?"

The girl seemed suddenly to come to life and shiver with excitement; but getting no reply she kept her thoughts to herself, and let them lead her to a cottage near the Abbey gatehouse where she was shown to a small room simply furnished with a bed, a chair and a blanket, not so different from her one-time cell. The women of the cottage spoke no English, but they produced a change of clothes, clean but unflattering. She was too tired to attempt any more French. For the first time in days Agnes slept deeply.

Some days passed. There was no news of Bertram or Edward, even when Agnes revealed her true family name. But the reaction of Guilbert and Walter was remarkable when she said cautiously "There is one other religious my mother has asked me to inquire after, an old family friend who I have heard may have been attached to Abbey Dorsley. We do not know if he is alive or dead, or what happened to him after the Abbey was sacked. My mother would be glad to have news of him to pass on to his family, if he is in hiding in France."

"And his name, my daughter?"

"His name in the world, before he took vows, was Robert Woodward, the son of a glover."

Guilbert and Walter exchanged surprised glances.

"Daughter Agnes, you have just missed meeting Brother Robert. He was visiting here in Jumieges a week ago, but now we think he is back in England. He is no longer professed, so he is free to travel wherever he wishes."

A strong tremor shook Agnes. " I am so happy to hear he is alive and well. Please tell me how to get in touch with him – he may have news of my father." This last was added as an afterthought.

The Abbey Dorsley superiors explained that Robert had arrived unexpectedly, riding a borrowed horse, to exchange information about Brother Leo and others of the Abbey Dorsley community still in England, and to take back news and instructions from Guilbert and Walter, as the senior surviving members of the community. "We believe he may have joined Brother Leo somewhere not far from Dorsley; it seems they are both employed at a great house . Sadly, you would have learned more if he had still been here."

Agnes nodded. "I must now return to my mother. My humblest thanks to you both for this good news."

"But you must certainly not travel alone. As it happens there are staying here two former members from Abbey Dorsley – you would not know them – and we will ask them to escort you at least as far as the coast. It might not be wise for him to cross the Channel, but he can see you safely on a boat for England."

In this way Agnes found herself riding to the coast, not on an apple cart, but in a relatively comfortable wagon with Daniel and Septimus, and exchanging her story for theirs.

They were intrigued to hear that a young Englishwoman from a good family (and a former nun, as they discovered by close questioning) could have travelled alone in disguise hundreds of miles on much the same route that they had covered a month or so earlier; and this without apparently coming to any harm – as they said "Our Lady must have had special care of you in these lawless times and strange places, among rough men, otherwise you could not have survived."

To which Agnes replied "I never felt I was in danger. Indeed God has been good to me."

Septimus was unimpressed by the nun turned peasant girl, but Daniel, gentle and concerned by nature, paid close attention to her story and assured her Robert was almost certainly still alive.

"We will send messages ahead of you so that when you land in England you may be able to trace your father and brother. Perhaps Robert will have heard of their whereabouts. This map I have drawn for you will help you find your way to the Cotswolds. I sincerely hope there may be kindly travellers who will help you on your way."

Agnes in turn was touched by the kindness of the artist-monk whose delicately drawn map, with its symbols and exquisite lettering, was to act as a talisman on her long journey home.

The girl's story as she told it to Walter Lefevre

As I think you have guessed, I was for some years in the convent of an enclosed order. My name as a sister I think it best not to tell you, for fear it may bring discredit on the good and holy women of the

Order. I accepted the discipline and the duties, but always I felt unworthy. There were sisters who followed the Rule with their whole hearts, but my devotion was not total. A small part of me belonged still to the world. Believe me, I struggled to put these thoughts away, but may God forgive me, they kept returning. Then came a letter from my mother with heartbreaking news – about the vandalising of so many houses of God, the persecution of the faithful, the escape into hiding of lay members of my family who would not give up their faith . My mother's letter made me think long and deeply, and to question my own faith. Would I have put my life in danger as my father and brother did? Would I have denied my Lord, as Peter did, if I was tested? How could I with good conscience continue as a religious while my mother was left alone (for my sisters are married and have families of their own) and perhaps herself in danger?

The Mother Superior gave me permission to visit my mother for three days. She did not understand my dilemma. At home, among scenes familiar from my childhood, sitting with my mother, seeing her grief and anxiety, I knew what I had to do. It was not an easy thing, to renounce my solemn vows. I read the Revelations of Dame Julian, who was a model for many in our Order. I prayed to Our Lord and Our Lady for guidance. I prayed for a sign to tell me what to do. On the third day the sign came. It is something too private for me to talk about. I still have moments of terrible doubt, but it is too late to turn back.

My mother gave me her blessing when I set out. She was afraid for me, but she did nothing to stop me. I am sometimes stubborn, and I do not always listen to advice. These are worldly failings. I have spiritual faults too. Perhaps I would have abandoned my vocation sooner or later even if events had not driven me to it. I dressed as a working woman, a seamstress, because I am used to sewing, and rode south on a borrowed horse with my father's steward to look after me. As we rode we heard about the desecration of Abbey Dorsley and Glastonbury. We heard that some of the brothers had escaped to France and it seemed possible my father and brother had done that too, since there was no other news of them. After two weeks we came to the harbour of Poole, in Dorset, and lodged there at a tavern, the Three Tuns, pretending to be father and daughter, while Ralph inquired about boats to cross the Channel.

He learned of two fishermen who would now and then cross to France to sell their catch, mackerel and lobsters. Ralph gave them a large sum of money to smuggle me on board, telling them I was a French girl whose husband had died on a trading visit to England, that I needed to get home but had no papers. That way I would not have to talk to the fishermen. It was smelly on that boat, I can tell you, among the piles of fish, and damp and cold. Mostly I hid under tarpaulins. It wasn't possible to sleep, and some of the time I was very sick. I don't care to remember that crossing. I didn't believe we would ever reach France safely, but at dawn on the fourth day the men made me understand that the harbour we'd sighted was Le Havre and the great river was the Seine.

They began to land their catch, rolling the fish in barrels down planks and so on to handcarts. I could overhear other men saying the carts would carry the fish to market. I came ashore and paid the men some more. Ralph had found me some French money, I don't know how, and he told me fifty francs was worth a sovereign. I was careful not to speak in French (or English, for that matter) and no one took much notice of me. So I followed the carts inland, on foot, till they came to the market. What a sight! I had seen nothing like it in England.

Crowds of farmers and fishermen shouted their wares, selling from barrows or handcarts or barrels. There were giant cheeses and sides of beef and tubs full of vegetables. It was frightening, the noise and hustle. I felt like running away, but Our Lady led me to a stall of apples with two motherly women selling. I made signs that I needed to ride on a cart to Abbaye Jumieges, pretending I was deaf and dumb (I wrote Jumieges on the hem of my gown with a piece of charcoal.) After a while they seemed to understand. The older woman called over a young fellow, perhaps her son, and I heard her mention Jumieges several times. I showed the man some money – I was careful not to let go of it – and he helped me climb up on to a cart laden with apples they'd just sold, I think. The driver was an old man who asked no questions and didn't try to talk. I kept up the deaf and dumb pretence. After a few hours we drove through this gateway here, and I guessed this must be Abbaye Jumieges.

When Walter Lefevre had listened carefully to her account he asked Agnes three questions: did she understand a little French? Would she trust Daniel and Septimus to see her as far as the coast, and put her on a ship? Had she enough money to make her way home? To them all she answered a trusting and straightforward yes.

XIII

DANIEL' S RETURN

All guests who present themselves are to be welcomed as Christ ...Once a guest has been announced, the Superior and the Brothers are to meet him with all the courtesy of love. Great care and concern are to be shown in receiving poor people and pilgrims.

The Rule of St Benedict in English, chapter 53

When I left Southampton on that stormy autumn day I never dreamed I would be returning within a month or two. I had believed England was no longer safe for me; that my future lay in France, where I would be able to carry on at least in part my life as a monk, and perhaps my illuminating, if God willed it. Septimus had been my guide and mentor, but I could not expect that to continue. He had his own life to lead, probably following the family tradition as a land agent, under an assumed name. Abbaye Jumieges seemed a safe refuge where I could pick up the threads of my vocation and consider the future.

Indeed I was deeply contented there at first, learning French, helping the monks in various domestic tasks, finding a niche in the community. Their school of illuminating was different from ours, and it would take a while for me to adapt my style and methods. But I did not doubt everything would be possible in time.

Then the girl arrived. Her story was a sad one, of a missing father and brother, renounced vows. The strangest part was her failure to meet Brother Robert whom she had known as a child, she said. At first I was not sure if I believed it all – her journey from England to the Abbaye seemed inconceivable. And yet it was not so very different from ours. I am not used to women, having no sisters, and enclosed at Abbey Dorsley for seven years. So it was difficult for me to ask her questions, though I felt strangely curious about her story. How did it feel, I wondered, to spend years in a convent and then to enter the world in such difficult and unhappy circumstances? Would she come to regret having renounced her vows? Did she not long for the peace and security of the religious life?

When the Prior asked us if we would escort Sister Agnes, as we were told to call her, to the French coast and find her a safe passage across the Channel, at first we were inclined to say no.

We were concerned not to be discovered by local people as refugees from an English monastery, possibly unwelcome strangers, and religious (one of us at least) travelling with a woman. Talking it over, Septimus and I felt there would be disapproval of our odd little party. None of us spoke much French, and Sister Agnes was a virgin who might attract unwelcome attention from men. But she was clearly in some distress, having made the difficult journey from England alone, and now strangely anxious to return again. She talked to Septimus more freely than to me, perhaps because he was more a layman, and he began to suspect that her distress was due to a former relationship. He guessed that she had come all this way from home not only to seek her father and brother, but in search of someone else: whether man or woman he could not learn. Septimus also had it in mind to return to England, and he half persuaded me that I should go with him, at least for a short while, to see if we could recover some of my precious manuscripts and collect writing materials – pigments particularly – that were not easily available at Jumieges. Sister Agnes was almost in tears at the prospect of having to cross the Channel again alone.

So I allowed myself to be persuaded, promising the Jumieges community that I would soon be back with materials useful to them too. They loaded us with provisions for the journey, with French wine and cheeses as presents for any English religious we might meet (here I was mindful of Brother Leo at his hermitage in the Deer Park, described for us in much detail by Robert Woodward.) One plan I had hazily in mind was to locate Brother Leo, to visit him secretly with gifts and hope to hear news of other Abbey Dorsley survivors. For I was missing my former Cistercian colleagues and longed to see again Brother Leo, who had been like an uncle to some of the younger monks.

They saddled three horses for us: Sister Agnes told us she had been used to riding before she entered her convent, and we were well provisioned with gifts for any who might help us. They gave us exact directions to reach the coast, partly following the broad river called Seine, at a small port named Honfleur. There they had arranged for a fishing boat to take us across the Channel (which they call La Manche, their word for sleeve, because of its shape, I suppose) provided conditions were right and we were prepared to pay handsomely for the crossing. All in all it seemed churlish of me to refuse, and Septimus was quite positive we should not.

We set out on a chilly spring morning, looking back gratefully at the Jumieges people who had given us such hospitality. Septimus and Agnes I knew did not expect to return, but I had made up my mind that failing Abbey Dorsley this would be my future monastic home, a place where I could know peace and inspiration for my art.

At Honfleur four fishermen met us and helped us aboard a small but sturdy boat, the *Grace de Dieu*, sturdier than the one Septimus and I had crossed from Southampton in. They were mackerel fishermen, quite rough fellows with no English, and I was nervous for Sister Agnes; but she seemed to accept all the hazards quite placidly. The sailors set a course for Plymouth Sound on the coast of Devon, where they had fished before. This was considerably west of where we had hoped to land, but we were not consulted and clearly we were in their hands. I had heard of Plympton Priory, an Augustinian house owning a lot of land thereabouts, given by local gentry; but I did not know if it had survived the terrible times.

The weather was reasonable so the crossing should take less than two days – but, oh, the stench of fish and the discomfort of a working boat not built for passengers.

Often I found myself sympathising with Agnes.

"Sister, this must be worse for you than for us. Have you faced conditions like these before?"

Her reply took me by surprise.

"Indeed, Brother Daniel, I came to France in a fishing boat. I knew what to expect, and believe me this is no worse for me than for you. Do you suppose because I am a woman I am timid and feeble?"

"I beg your pardon, Sister. I did not mean to suggest any such thing; but I have no sisters, and I was brought up to believe that women lead more tranquil and ordered lives than we men."

"Can anything be more tranquil and ordered than the life of a monk?"

"There you have a point; but mine was neither tranquil nor ordered after we left Dorsley."

"Brother Daniel, I was forgetting the travails you had after the Abbey was attacked. Forgive me for being insensitive. And you must remember that before I took my vows I lived a very adventurous life, with a lively family of brothers and sisters. We used to ride and go fishing and hawking and swimming. The sea does not frighten me. But I think perhaps you do not swim ?"

"Not at all. Indeed I had never seen the sea until Septimus and I came to Southampton."

After that we talked quite a lot, Agnes and I, about her childhood, her family and her life in the convent. I was bold enough to ask why she had renounced her vows, but she put me in my place, very politely, by saying that was something she did not wish to talk about. In turn she asked me why I had been professed, and how I had discovered my talent for illuminating (this she learned about from Septimus.) And she told me of her gift for embroidering, as one of her chosen tasks at the convent. We agreed that art and embroidering go hand in hand. In those three days I talked more freely than I had ever done to any woman, and I fancied that Agnes responded very willingly.

"And your life from now onwards, Brother Daniel? Will you stay at Jumieges and become a master craftsman, teaching others ?"

This caught me unawares. Was this what I wanted, or were there some other horizons to be explored?

If I was honest with myself the enclosed life might not satisfy all my wishes, though I was clear that my future lay in some form of art. I needed Septimus's judgement and his practical approach to matters.

We learned it would not be the most direct crossing, but a trip they made regularly with mackerel and sardines, bringing back building stone and timber. These were strong rough men, rather threatening in appearance and coarse in speech. Although Agnes had good French, as far as I could tell, she found it difficult to communicate with them, and they made it obvious they regarded a female passenger as an encumbrance. Agnes's previous stoicism crumbled and she was near to tears.

"Daniel and Septimus, I do not feel safe with these men. I'm not welcome on board. Suppose they attack me at sea? I've no support, nothing to defend myself with. Yet I must return to my mother and continue the search for my family. I can't give up now. Advise me, please."

Septimus and I conferred. This was an embarrassing situation for us. We argued a bit, Septimus suggesting we looked for another boat, while I leaned towards riding back to Jumieges to find some of the lay people who might go with her. In the end of course we decided we had no choice but to escort her back to England ourselves, paying the Norman fishermen twice what had originally been agreed, though it was not at all what I'd intended. Indeed I could have wept at leaving the peace and security of Jumieges just when I felt my problems were over. Nonetheless the three of us set out on a stormy day towards the coast of Devon, 200 miles away; and I have to admit I felt deeply uneasy.

XIV

A WELCOME IN WALES

Give them a wilderness or forest … . And in a few years you will find a dignified abbey in the midst of smiling plenty.

Giraldis Cambrensis, *c.* 1180

W hen I saw these two draggled barefoot children – I thought they were children – struggling up to the Abbey gate at Tintern I was reminded of my own arrival here. I must have cut a sorry sight, as they did, and I doubt any poor folk would have taken me in, looking like a vagabond who'd lately escaped from a village jail. I called the gatekeeper and asked him to give them a night's bed and shelter, for the love of our Saviour. They were led away to be succoured, as the practice is with good Cistercians when folk come begging, and I saw no more of them till next day.

It needs must be explained that I've been made more than welcome here, for many reasons. First they needed not so much a miller (and this did frustrate me a good deal) but more an assistant brewer and baker, and these were tasks I could turn my hand to at a pinch. Next they had heard terrible reports of the tragedy at Dorsley, not too greatly overplayed, and third they were full of compassion for any who'd survived that massacre. As a fellow Cistercian it was easy for me to settle into their routine, and make myself useful. I found the Welsh language hard to make out, but most of the brothers spoke some English, and the Mass was still sung in Latin. I'm not a musical man myself, but I found the familiar words and tunes comforting.

They told me the first White monks came here from L'Aumone in the north of France about 50 years before they came to Dorsley. So this place was well set up by Walter FitzRichard, Lord of Chepstow, by the time the Berkeleys built Dorsley. Now this Walter was related to Bishop William of Winchester, who first gave the White Monks a home in England. Then Tintern became the first Welsh House. A famous writer among the Welsh – they call him Gerald of Wales – said the Cistercians anywhere could turn a wilderness or forest into "smiling plenty." Here they follow the Rule of St Benedict pretty closely, though not so rigidly that I couldn't fit in with their daily life. And though the lansdcape hereabouts is not at all like our Cotswold hills (though it's remote as we used to be) I feel at home in this steep river valley with woods on both sides. As for work, I'm thankful to be allowed to brew some ale and bake a loaf or two to pay for my keep, as it were. The monks here live comfortably, which suits me.

I'd only been at Tintern a week or two when news came of others who'd escaped and found refuge in various places.

A Tintern brother who'd been visiting sick relatives in Somerset had heard of a layman from Dorsley who'd gone into hiding for a while on a farm near Glastonbury, or rather what remained of that other sad vandalised abbey. I heard later that most of the brethren were driven out, their Abbot most savagely executed and buildings ill-treated as they were with us at Dorsley. Still, at Glastonbury they kept their hospice and made poor travellers welcome, though not if they openly travelled as pilgrims. The King, God forgive him, had said pilgrimages were a Popish practice, not to be continued, and the famous shrines were to be closed down. What on earth would our good Guestmaster and Infirmarian have said about that? The Tintern brother offered to bring a message secretly to me, and when it reached me I learned the writer was Robert Woodward, our former groom who'd been deprived of his membership of the Order for riotous living, or so I believed. Unfrocked or no, I was pleased beyond words to get this letter from Robert, from one of the old community. He wrote:

Dear Brother Wilfrid, I am glad indeed to hear you are well and living with the brothers at Tintern. Many of us had wondered how you fared after you fled for your life from Dorsley, and we feared the worst. I am sending this letter by hand of a trust-worthy messenger who will not reveal your whereabouts to any who might cause trouble for you. Thomas Cromwell's men are still roaming the countryside like wolves looking for whom they may devour. Destroy this letter as soon as you can, and do not tell any you have heard from me. I am acting as go-between for several of the brethren, but we want no record left of our contacts. We are an invisible network.

Now I have news of others who will rejoice to know you are safe. Br. Theodore and Br. Francis have settled in villages not a hundred miles from Dorsley, and we hear they may accept posts as parish priests where there is a need. I'm sure no small flock could have more devoted shepherds; we all pray for them. Prior Guilbert and Guestmaster Walter escaped safely to France, and I have been to see them at our sister community of Jumieges. It is a place of great beauty, and no one could blame them for travelling no farther. But they feel a duty to try to bring some of the old fraternity together and in time build up a new Abbey Dorsley, when all this trouble is over. No one knows if their hopes can be realised. Br. Joseph, our carpenter, has found work (under another name) in the abbey at Tewkesbury, where the towns-people have formed a task force to preserve the building for the town and keep it alive as a place of worship. There is much work to be done, and Br. Joseph's skills are daily in demand.

As for my old friend and father-confessor, Br. Leo, he is living a very quiet and devout life on a great estate to the south of Abbey Dorsley, where he is gardener, beekeeper and poultryman. A new house is being built as a country place for one of the King's courtiers. The lord and lady of the mansion know and respect Leo's Catholic faith, but he lives as a hermit in the grounds and is almost as much a recluse as he was at Dorsley. I am able to see him as I have work there too, in the stables, but I have freedom to travel also – I must not reveal my connection with the noble family, but you may guess how useful it is – so I have permission to visit France soon on a mission for Sir Nicholas. I am serving as a groom, I am helping Brother Leo as best I can, and I plan to bring the Prior and the Guestmaster whatever news I can of our former colleagues. I am like a carrier pigeon !

And for you, my old friend Wilfrid, let me have your news too as soon as you can find a trustworthy messenger to bring it to my uncle's farm in Somerset. I enclose the address, but you must memorise and burn it.

Destroy this letter quickly. God be with you and keep you safe – Robert Woodward.

I have destroyed the letter, as he instructed, but I remember every word. I feel less lonely now that I know others survived from Abbey Dorsley, but I have said nothing of this to the Tintern folk.

Now to tell more about the newcomers at the Abbey. Next morning they appeared not at the first Office of the Day, but at Prime, decently dressed though not in monastic habits. Imagine my amazement when I recognised the one I thought to be a boy as our own Brother Daniel. He did not notice or recognise me, and I was mighty puzzled to know whether I should greet him by name or keep our identities secret. In any case I could not talk to him in the presence of a woman; I did not know her, it would not have been seemly, and I guessed he had not told her who he truly was.

Twenty-four hours passed before it was possible to speak to him alone, in the hour of recreation.

"Daniel, can it be you? This is Wilfrid the miller: you remember me?"

Daniel's sudden shock and then his pleasure were wonderful to see.

"Brother Wilfrid, dear friend! How do you come to be here at Tintern? Are you well? Has God been good to you?"

"Indeed He has, far more good than I deserve, for I committed a grave crime at Dorsley. But here I am, settled and I hope a useful member of the fraternity here. Tell me your own story – I guess times have been hard for you."

I longed to know who the woman was, of course, and what adventures brought them here together, but I judged it best to let Daniel tell me his story in his own way. And a strange story it was.

It seems that after they left Abbey Jume-something (I think I have the name right, but I am no scholar) Daniel and the lay brother Septimus felt guilty at letting the woman travel alone and unprotected with a villainous looking ship's crew. So they handed over a bag full of coins which they could ill afford to part with, and joined the fishing crew as extra hands. These two lads were unused to manual labour of any kind, and I dare say the fishermen gave them a rough time. Conditions on board were harsh, the salty food almost uneatable, and the men's language enough to shock any well brought up young men, let alone a gentlewoman. Just as well they understood few of the profanities, and they were able to shield the woman from the worst of the fishermen's crudeness.

Three days out from Honfleur a violent storm blew up and the men struggled to keep the ship on course. As the wind became stronger and the waves higher they were forced to throw some of their cargo overboard. Still the ship listed, and took in a great deal of water. Daniel and Septimus were obliged to exert themselves as they never had before, and Agnes (this I learned was her real name) lay in the hold, terribly seasick. This went on for three more days, and it became obvious they were far from landing at Plymouth. Indeed the south-westerly gale was driving them east towards a headland which Daniel later heard called Start Point, a graveyard for many fishing boats in sudden winter storms. The French fishermen were unfamiliar with this stretch of coast, they had no chart to locate rocks, and their boat, the Grace de Dieu, was leaking beyond repair. This was what Daniel told me:

"Septimus and I had no seamanship skills, so we were made to try to plug the leaks with our bare hands, and to pull on ropes too frayed for a proper grip. All the time the noise of the wind and crashing waves made it impossible to hear ourselves talk. I have never been so frightened or worked so hard in all my life. I felt sure we would all die. What happened next was the most terrifying thing of all. A great grinding and smashing noise, and water poured all over the decks and up to our waists. The Frenchmen shouted "Les rochers ! Les rochers! Quittez le bateau ! Chacun pour lui-meme|" Somehow they made us understand the boat was breaking up and we should try to scramble ashore. Then I remembered Agnes, sick and cold with terror down below. I leaned down and managed to catch hold of her clothing. I dragged her by sheer force up on deck, then pulled her into the icy waters with me. We landed on smooth slimy rocks with no foothold. As far as I can remember I just slithered across the rocks to where I supposed there might be a beach, pulling Agnes with me, both of us shouting for Septimus.

The crashing of waves on the rocks and the roar of the wind blotted out all other noises. At one stage I heard him calling for us, I thought a long way off. He seemed to be shouting for help: "Save me, dear Lord and Father." I could just hear Agnes praying, and I think I too called on our Lord for mercy. For a while I thought I could faintly hear Septimus's voice, then the sound faded. I never saw him again." Daniel's voice broke and he was not able to speak for a time. Then he continued his story, but with pauses when he sobbed and groaned. I could not find a way to comfort him.

"After perhaps half an hour scrambling about on the rocks, I couldn't tell how long, Agnes and I clambered off the rocks into a kind of cave under a cliff. It seemed to be above the water level, and dry from a fair way up. Later they told us the water in this cave sometimes reached above a man's height, but we were able to stand with water only up to our waists. It was icy cold and getting to be dark. We held on to each other and prayed: there was nothing else we could do. Agnes amazed me with the power of her supplications.

Imagine, dear Wilfrid, imagine our amazement when we heard voices and the sound of oars. A small English rowing boat drifted near the cave entrance. We never found out who they were or how they survived the storm, but our rescuers said something confused about a smugglers' cove and searching for wrecks in the gale. The storm was dying down now; they heard our screams, rowed into the cave and pulled us on board, half dead with cold and fright. It astonished me that Agnes, with her gentle ladylike background, had the stamina to battle through; I was surprised at myself too. The two oarsmen took us to a harbour – they called the place Dartmouth – and between them they half-carried us to an inn. I did not care to ask if they were in fact smugglers or those people who scavenge from wrecks - it was enough to know they had surely saved our lives, saints in our eyes. I wished I had English money to give them as a reward, but I had lost all my few possessions in the wreck. They seemed to be known at the inn, and ale and pies were put before them.

The innkeeper's wife wrapped us in blankets and poured a hot drink down us (brandy, I believe; Agnes was very upset when she learned next day what the fiery spirit was called.). The inn was the Flying Angel, with a sign like a ship's figurehead, and that innkeeper's wife was an angel as far as we were concerned.

After a day and a night in warm dry beds, fed fish stew by the land-lady, we told her we would be eternally grateful and asked God's blessing on her, but more than this we could not offer, being desti-tute ourselves. Mercifully she did not ask too many questions. We did not of course reveal our true identities. What would that good woman have made of an unprofessed nun and a monk on the run? We asked in vain for news of Septimus. Besides the two of us, only one French fisherman had been picked up alive from the wreck of the Grace de Dieu. May God rest the soul of my good companion Septimus and the others who perished that night. He was my dear friend and I shall miss him more than I can say. As time goes on the hurt gets worse."

I listened marvelling at Daniel and the woman's adventure, but there was no opportunity then to hear more about their misery. Later they told me in snatches about their difficult and dangerous journey, trying to get across country, penniless, making for Agnes's home or the ruins of Abbey Dorsley. The landlady provided clothes belonging to her young son for Agnes, whose own clothes had been ruined after the wreck. The town where they now found themselves was a huddle of small grey stone houses straggling on either side of the river Dart. They crossed the river by a ferry (a rowing boat not much bigger than the one they'd been rescued in) because there was no bridge this far downstream. One thing they noticed, the redness of the water, I guess from local red sandstone. Then they pressed ahead on foot, keeping to narrow roads across the moor. They heard of several former religious houses in the area, mostly alien houses of French monks, and also the houses and parklands belonging to local noblemen; but they dared not stop in case their disguises gave them away (I did not see how that could possibly be, but the couple are young and frightened for their lives.)

Here and there they had help from a parish priest or the owner of an inn, and so they made their way in short stages to the outskirts of Bristol, and from there by ferry to the coast of Wales. They judged this would be safer than travelling through the seaport of Bristol, where King's men would be lodging. The ferry crossing they paid for by helping the crew, Agnes being still dressed as a boy.

I advised them to stay a while at Tintern till they were stronger and less shocked, but they both were minded to travel on: Daniel wishing to make his way somehow back to France, Agnes still seeking news of her father and brother, dead or alive. So I had to consider how best to help them onwards, both safely and secretly. (I had still said nothing of my contact with Robert Woodward.) The Cistercian brothers spoke of a herd of Welsh cattle soon to be driven into England, to be sold at one of the Midland markets. "Now", I said, "if you two would dress as farm labourers, claiming to know little of the world, you might be allowed to travel with the drovers. But I advise you, Mistress Agnes, to continue in the disguise of a boy, for greater safety on the road. Both the drovers and the travellers you might meet would have little respect for a loose woman, as (God forbid) they might suppose you to be."

Daniel asked "Is there no other way? I am nervous as to who we might meet, and we are both tired of disguises."

"I can see no other way, Brother, so long as you are anxious for your true identities not to be found out. Without money you cannot pay your way, can you? The brothers here will give you a letter to be presented at any religious house on the way, but there's not much likelihood of the cattle drovers putting up at such a place. They sleep for the most part with their animals, at the roadside or in barns. I shall do my best to get messages to any in England who might know the whereabouts of former Abbey Dorsley men, or of Agnes's family. But I warn you both not to expect much joy. One more thing: here is a rough map of the way I came to Tintern, in case you meet any who helped me on the road. There was a Gloucester man, a lawyer, who was a good Samaritan to me. Here is how to get in touch with him, if you should find yourselves anywhere near Gloucester. Now God be with you, dear young folk, and I'll wait to hear news of you from my secret friends."

It was a cruel late spring when they set off, and bitter weather with Welsh fogs and frosts. I watched the cattle with their herders plodding towards the English border, and prayed for the safety of those two young people. Then I wrote to Robert Woodward. I'm not much of hand at writing, so it was short and not fancy:

"Greetings from Tintern to one who was my fellow worker at the place we knew well. I think it is best not to name people or places. I am sending this, as you said I should, to a farm where they know you, and I hope it will reach you quickly. I have news you will be glad to hear. Daniel the artist and a friend he met in France are sheltering here in Wales, but they set out tomorrow for England. Septimus is dead, drowned on the way from France. Daniel's friend seeks a father and brother who may be hiding in the south of England. I know you will do your best to help these dear people if they come your way. They are travelling with a large party of cattle drovers, heading first for Gloucester, calling themselves Ralph and Roger. I have not told them I am writing this, for safety's sake. Your good friend, Wilfrid."

This letter I entrusted, as before, to a lay brother with relatives living in Somerset. Then I could only hope, and wait for news. It did my heart good to have helped those two young people in a small way (though I cannot say I approved of the risks this young woman was taking; finding her family was a task for a man, surely) and to learn that there were Dorsley men safe in France. One day I hope God will bring us all together again – those of us still living – and in the meantime I'm thankful to grind my flour, bake my bread, serve the community here, and say my prayers without hindrance.

XV

REFUGE AT THE DEER PARK

The fourth step of humility is that in obedience under difficult, unfavour-
able or even unjust conditions his heart quietly embraces suffering and
endures it without weakening or seeking escape.

The Rule of St Bendict in English, chapter 7

Here I am still in my home, or rather my hermitage, thanking
God for life and health, saying the Mass to myself each day,
busy with my garden and my bees, and looking forward always to
young Robert's visits. It is a cruel spring and freezing most nights,
but with the firewood I'm allowed to gather in the deer park I can
keep a fire going day and night, and I'm well sheltered from the
south west storms that whistle up the estuary and at times bring
down trees, ancient oaks and beeches. Truth to tell I'm more cosy
here than I was in winter in my damp cell at Dorsley.

It's true I'm getting old and ache somewhat in my bones, but this is
a small offering to give God for his goodness. Sir Nicholas and Lady
Poyntz suffer me to please myself in the garden. While it's winter with

little growing and the bees asleep, I can spend more time meditating and tending the goat and the geese. Lady Felicity visits from time to time and she brings me little gifts: a woollen blanket, an extra hood and cloak against the cold, an ivory crucifix to replace the one that was broken. She told me it came from Italy, given to her by an ambassador. It's astonishing that someone who moves in such distinguished society should trouble herself about me. My conscience rebukes me for accepting these luxuries, but I find it exceedingly difficult to say no to Lady Felicity. She could charm the birds off the trees.

And lately there have been more old friends arriving here, so that I can hardly call myself a hermit any more. Let me think over the events of the last few days, and make a note of them at the back of my Missal – may God forgive me for putting it to such an unholy use. Robert paid a flying visit to say he had heard from Brother Wilfrid, safe in Wales at the abbey of Tintern. Wilfrid was not the most contemplative of us at Abbey Dorsley, but nonetheless good hearted and generous. I was pleased to hear he is back at his milling, and keeping the Rule. More surprising was Robert's other news: Wilfrid was sending on here two old friends – he did not name them – looking for a quiet place to redirect themselves and perhaps start a new life. I would know one of them, and the other was much in need of a father confessor. So of course I was mighty curious to know who these travellers might be.

A week or two passed until I heard more: the two travellers would be reaching the Deer Park disguised as drovers, calling themselves Roger and Ralph, bringing cattle across the Severn on their way to Oxford.

And so they appeared on foot, travel-stained and footsore, on a March morning at the turn of the year.(I compute the seasons by sun and moon rise, and that year there was a full moon on Our Lady's Day.) I did not know how to accommodate them, but they asked only to spend a night in the Deer Park stables, and this was arranged through my friend the head groom. The taller of the two drew me to one side.

"Brother Leo, surely you remember me, Daniel the illustrator?"

"*Daniel?* But I heard you drowned going across to France?"

"I nearly drowned more than once, but God was good to me. My dear Septimus, God rest his soul, was swept on to the rocks off the coast of Devon and we did not see him again. I grieve for him, Brother, for he was a dear friend and I cannot express his kindness to me. Pray for him, Brother, and for me that I did not save him."

"I will indeed say *Requiescat in pace* many times in his memory. May he rest in peace in the deep sea. But tell me your story, Daniel, for I guess there is much to tell."

We sat in my small hermitage – a cave, really, in the limestone escarpment, below my Lady Poyntz's garden; and there Daniel poured out his heart, his grief and needless sense of guilt at all that had happened to him since he left Abbey Dorsley. It was not such a terrible story, after all, and his account of the Abbey Jumieges made me feel the survivors of our little community might be restored and renewed there. On the outskirts of Gloucester, while the drovers sheltered in the forest, they made contact with Wilfrid's Good Samaritan, the lawyer Samuel Ford, who gave them a sum of money, good advice about travelling in the area (where many King's men lodged, and followers of the Protestant faith who might inform on a disguised monk). So once again the Dorsley survivors had reason to be grateful to him.

Then came the revelations about Daniel's companion, and I confess I found it very hard to accept that a nun who had renounced her vows could behave with such boldness and lack of decorum. But who was I to condemn a young woman whose unhappiness I could not begin to fathom? Daniel asked if he could bring her to talk to me at the hermitage next day, and at first I was unable to say yes. Here was an unthinkable situation: a young woman and I alone together; a woman disguised as a man; a former religious who had, as it seemed, to me, turned her back on God. But Daniel persuaded me that her need of a father figure (for she had still not traced her missing family) was greater than my embarrassment at listening to her.

Agnes came to me at noon, after the time I set aside for Terce, wearing now a rough skirt under a long cloak, and hooded so that her face was almost hidden. I could not spy out her face or figure, nor did I wish to. It would have been unseemly. Straightaway she knelt down on the bare earth.

"Father Leo, bless me and forgive me my sins, for they are many. *Mea maxima culpa.*"

"My daughter, we are all sinners. It is not my duty to chastise you in your sadness."

"May I tell you everything? I have a desperate need to confess."

"My daughter, I am here to listen to whatever you choose to tell me."

So I heard Agnes's tale. I think there was nothing she held back, not even her overpowering love for Robert Woodward whom she had known first as a child. Sometimes she cried, sometimes twisted in her fingers the cloth of her skirt, sometimes put her hands together as if in prayer. It was a pitiful tale, not least because she felt she could not permanently return to her mother and sisters as one who had (these were her own words) abandoned God and her vocation.

She had come too far, she said, ever to resume the way of life of Sister Hildegarde; and she owed it to her family not to come home until she had news of her father and brother, whom increasingly she believed to be dead.

"My daughter, have you told Robert of your feelings?"

"Father, I have not seen him in all the years since I entered the convent. However there was not a single day when I did not think of him, and pray for him."

"But you have written letters?"

" A few, but there was very little personal in them."

"So perhaps he has no idea how it is with you?"

"I am sure he does not guess. Please give me absolution, Father, even though I do not deserve it."

"I am to believe that since you left the convent you have committed no sinful act?"

"Not deeds. But I have sinful thoughts. Many and wicked."

So I gave her Our Lord's blessing and forgiveness, and tried to assuage some of her self-abasement. In the meanwhile I arranged for Daniel and Agnes to stay a few nights with my friend the shepherd and his wife, presenting them (Heaven forgive me) as brother and sister. As soon as this was arranged I sent a message to Robert; though I never knew when he would arrive, or where he might be between visits, he had given me an address for letters to be sent on. I told him as little as I thought strictly necessary. I asked him if he could acquire drawing materials and needlework silks so that the two young people could resume a few of their vocational skills and so perhaps regain their self-respect. It was still unclear to me if Robert knew who they both were, or if he guessed.

The three of them met here at the Deer Park on Ash Wednesday. It was Lent again, a period of fasting for me and I hoped of repentance for all of them. I made a simple meal of fish and eggs, and because it was an unseasonably warm day – the bees were venturing out – we ate in the orchard. I could sense that it was a remarkable day for all of them. Daniel showed us a sketch for a manuscript he planned to give the monks at Jumieges, as a thank offering, and I could see (even though I have no knowledge of art) that it was a thing of beauty.

Agnes drew back her hood when she asked my blessing once again, and I felt her whole personality had changed now that she was seeing Robert after so many years. Robert was reticent with them both; the situation was a difficult one for him to accept. I suspect he thought Agnes and Daniel were lovers.

Once or twice Agnes touched Robert. There was no doubting her attachment to him, but he did not (as far I could tell) respond. She said only a few shy words, looking down at her feet, and he spoke quite formally to her, as one might to a distant acquaintance. Next day he announced he must travel to London – these visits were always mysterious to me – and came to say goodbye to me, as he never failed to do.

"Robert my son, I hope you will see Agnes again. She is a good woman, and still holds to her beliefs and practises her faith. She is, you must know, devoted to you, as she has been since you both were childhood friends. This was in part her reason for leaving the convent."

His face showed total amazement.

"You must be mistaken, Brother Leo. I know absolutely nothing of this. She has not said a word."

"Did she never in her letters give you the smallest hint?"

He shook his head, but I thought I saw him colour at the idea.

"I cannot believe she would have left the convent because of me. We enjoyed sport together and saw each other quite often as young people. Then we took up our vocations and any letters we exchanged were purely as old friends."

"Speak to her, my son, so that she does not suffer from doubt and uncertainty."

I do not know what they said to each other, but I do know they spent some time together before Robert set off for London; and it seemed to me this would be a well-chosen match, and one that would please their respective parents.

Soon after this Robert rode away, without saying when he would return. Agnes did not seek me out; I felt obliged to go to her at the shepherd's cottage. At first she was reluctant to see me.

"Agnes, my dear girl, are there matters troubling you?"

"Father, I have been very foolish in all sorts of ways, and now I must bear my sorrow alone."

"Can you share this sorrow with me? Try to think of me as a true father who would do all he could to help his daughter. Trust me. I will tell no one."

And then all her unhappiness poured out. Throughout her years in the convent she had kept to herself her love for Robert, believing this to be some kind of penance. I did not altogether understand what she was doing penance for, but it seemed to be a compound of guilt at having resisted her parents' wishes, distress at finding her vocation did not lessen her desire for Robert, and guilt at her inability to suppress what she recognised as sexual desire – something the Order of St Hildegard would have regarded as an unforgivable sin. Her feelings were so deeply confused that I did not know how to comfort her. How can a celibate older man enter into the innermost thoughts of a passionate young woman?

What became apparent as we talked was that she realised Robert did not in any way reciprocate her feelings. This had come as a profound shock. Although until now there had been no exchange of emotions, she had innocently always supposed that one day (she did not consider when or how) they would find a way to express mutual love.

Agnes talked and wept and constantly rebuked herself. I hoped at least that this outpouring might lessen her grief. On reflection it occurred to me that if she would not, I could write to Robert. For several days I pondered how best to communicate something of her feelings to Robert, while not embarrassing him or forcing him into any promise or commitment. If I wrote, the letter must be discreet and not at all critical.

When the brief letter had gone by hand of messenger, I set about trying to calm Agnes and divert her distress into some constructive activity. When illustrating materials arrived for Daniel, it struck me that Agnes, with her own artistic eye, might act as an assistant to him in mixing pigments, preparing brushes and so forth. It was agreed they should remain at the Deer Park in privacy, Daniel at the stables and Agnes with the shepherd and his wife, until the manuscript was nearly complete; that Agnes should then visit her mother and Daniel travel to see the parents of his lost Septimus, to tell him how their son had died. Both of them were anxious at the prospect of seeing possibly bereaved mothers and bringing them no good news. I did my best to persuade them this was what Our Lord would have them do, and he would guide them. Agnes and Daniel came to accept what I said – I advised them separately, each in the light of their special circumstances. For a while they were absorbed in the intricacy of the new manuscript, based on a New Testament text in Latin, incorporating trees and wild life such as might be seen in the area of Jumieges.

From the diary of Agnes Farrell

I am so unhappy and confused I do not know what to think. If it were possible to return to the Convent I could perhaps seek guidance from one of the Sisters. Brother Leo is kindness itself, but there are things I cannot tell him. When I think of Robert my body reacts as if he were holding me clasped in his arms. I do not know how to control this violent physical longing. Would sexual desire be more easily suppressed if I had not renounced my vows?

To seek some comfort I turn to the writings of Mother Julian, the anchoress who had visions and lived not so far from our

Convent, in her cell at Norwich. I never went there, but Sisters who went as pilgrims told me about a busy corner of the town, near markets and traders' precincts, near the great cathedral too (has it been destroyed now, I wonder?) where the anchoress's cell was squeezed between a church and a tanner's yard. There pilgrims a hundred years ago could speak to her and ask her blessing through a narrow window. So she did not really live as a solitary, since so many people visited her. But perhaps I am being uncharitable, for she found time when she was alone to write down all her meditations and visions of Our Lord, and who knows how much wisdom she passed on. As I understand it she experienced something like an ecstasy for her Lord. Perhaps this too was a kind of sexual longing.

Let me read and see if Julian has words of wisdom for me. When she was quite young she begged for three graces: to be always aware of Christ's passion, to experience sickness when she was thirty (Our Lord's age at his death), and to have three wounds (as she called them) – the wounds of contrition, compassion and love for God. They do say that when she was 30, and seemingly at the point of death, she received the Last Rites and instantly recovered. It was then she had her fifteen miraculous revelations, and these she wrote about in her Revelations of Divine Love. Can there be any message for me in Mother Julian's Revelations? She says God's love is with us even at times of extreme trial or suffering. God looks on all his creation with pity, not with blame for our shortcomings. Each of us has an overwhelming responsibilty to love God and to love our brothers and sisters.

It may be that my mind is closed because of sin, but I find it hard to share Julian's confidence. How can God lessen my personal pain? Yet many have found a new faith through her final words: "All shall be well, and all manner of thing shall be well." So may it be, Lord, for me and for those I love.

Now I must join Daniel to help him with his painting. It is a distraction and it gives me pleasure to watch him at work. With so much talent he must surely find his vocation again, here or in France.

138

XVI

A LETTER FROM
ROBERT TO LEO

*The seven gifts of the Holy Ghost, that are given to men and women
pledged to the joy of heaven, and leading their lives wisely in this world –
are: Wisdom, Understanding, Counsel, Strength, Intelligence, Mercy and
the fear of God.*

Richard Rolle of Hampole, *The Form of Perfect Living, c.* 1340

This letter sent from France to be delivered by hand to Brother Leo, the hermit living at Deer Park, near Bath.

My dear Leo, my Father-in-God:
As always you are in my thoughts and prayers. I have much to thank you for, both in guiding my spiritual life and keeping me on the right path after I abandoned my vocation. Only God knows how much I have strayed from that path, but I would have been an even greater sinner without your wise words. You have been more than father to me, and I am ever conscious how much I owe you in love and friendship.

So it is with a heavy heart I write in response to your letter. How I wish I could write words to cheer you and also Sister Agnes and Brother Daniel, as they still are in my mind. For Daniel, I can hear no news of the finding of Septimus, either living or dead, though I have been in touch with fishermen and others in Devon. This will hurt him deeply, for I know how close they were during their time at Abbey Dorsley, and after.

For Agnes, I cannot express enough my admiration and respect for her. When we enjoyed each other's company as young people there was no woman I liked better, and her taking of the veil made me respect her even more. She is a model of what a good woman should be., and I am sad that life has not been kind to her. But for love, that has never entered my thoughts towards her.

I know there are those who feel we were made for each other from childhood, and perhaps I should seek to repay the kindness of her parents to me, and her own goodness. But I must be honest with you, dear Brother Leo. Much as I admire Agnes it is as a cousin. And there is someone I do truly love, so I think I know what true love is. This woman returns my love, and we are exploring ways of being together always. More of this when we meet.

In the meanwhile I commend Agnes to your fatherly concern; whenever she comes to you I am sure you will act as her confessor and her spiritual guide, as you have always done for me. She is a woman of God, and deserves whatever happiness God can offer her.

Now for some news of our former brethren. Guilbert and Walter are settled among the Jumieges fraternity – Walter says the brethren are almost as lovable a bunch of rogues as those at Dorsley! – and I believe they will stay in France, unless conditions in England change greatly in the next few years. They say they feel the Protestant ascendancy makes England not a comfortable place for them. My fellow novices, Edmund and Geoffrey, have arrived here too; they also came on a fishing boat, with many difficulties and adventures, but unharmed.

They will write to tell you their tale. Here too is Benoit our Chamberlain, who you remember came long ago from France with the late lamented Abbot Godfrey; so he is at home again, and made much of by the Jumieges community.

If I have news of others I shall communicate it, but most of all I long to hear your news, dear Brother Leo, that you are well and content in your hermitage, with the bees and the fowls and the fish? Please let me know.

Your devoted Robert.

A reply from Leo to Robert

Indeed I was glad to hear good news of members of our fraternity, some in France and some in England. May God bless them in all their endeavours, as also I daily ask Him to bless you, dear boy. Now I too have some news: Wilfrid our excellent miller has settled over the border in Wales with a Cistercian Community who make him feel much at home – I will not write where he is, as he still feels his life to be in some danger even among friends.

He communicates that he enjoys life at the abbey mill where he is, and he is trying to curb his unruly tongue, his temper and his aggressiveness. Same old Wilfrid! I pray he may in the end no longer think of himself as a murderer – God has surely forgiven him his act of violence in defence of our beloved abbey.

The travellers you know of are still sheltering near me and still undecided about their futures. I believe you must meet them again and make your peace with the one who was once a Sister. Your letter grieved me very much, but I, who have never known what it is to be in love, cannot judge others. Your conscience must guide you.

At the Deer Park there have been many visitors, though they do not trouble me much. Lately Sir Nicholas has held some deer chases which his friends come to see. The noblemen and women are led up to the roof where there is an exceedingly good view of the chase, across the park. Several hundred roe deer – the English ones, with a white patch on the rump – are flushed out by Sir Nicholas's deerhounds: big shaggy grey dogs, bred for hunting. I cannot say I have wished to see the kill. The dogs bring down some of the slower animals and then these graceful creatures are ripped apart by the dogs or finished off by one of the park keepers with an arrow to the head. I saw this happen once, and I find it an abomination to deal thus with any of God's creatures, mostly for sport.

I daresay Lady Poyntz, who has a kind enough heart herself, would tell me I am too soft-hearted. She loves to watch the chase and she holds that the deer are needed for food; there are too many in the park, and it is harmless sport. I do not see it that way. After the spectacle of the chase, which they cheer and applaud, the guests come down to the banqueting hall for a feast of venison, which is praised as being fresh, of good flavour and exceedingly well cooked in Sir Nicholas's kitchens. I have told you the cook is kind to me and gives me bread or cheese she has made. I am careful not to ask her about the slow roasting of a whole deer on a spit; I know this is the procedure, with the spit turned by a boy who is paid a pittance for his labours. You will say, Robert, that I used to breed fish for the Abbot's table, and geese too; and I cannot easily defend my part in this practice. I would not do it now, but there seems to me less cruelty in catching a carp with a net, or quickly wringing the neck of a fowl, than in letting a handsome stag in full antler be torn apart by dogs. Perhaps I am inconsistent, and a sentimental old man.

One other old friend from Dorsley I have news of. You remember Brother Vincent, whose joinery was so much in demand, as well as his exquisite carved saints' figures and crucifixes? A pilgrim called here on his way to Hailes who had met a parish priest serving a small village community near Warwick. This priest, he said, had some connection with Dorsley and asked the pilgrim to look out for any Dorsley survivors he might encounter. This same pilgrim heard there was a hermit living at the Deer Park – and here he found me. God must have guided him to me. The parish priest he spoke of is none other than our own Vincent.

Through correspondence and news from other travellers I have pieced together Vincent's story. After discreetly leaving Dorsley he made for Bath and joined some wool merchants riding towards the Midlands on the Fosse Way. He had a little money given him by our Guestmaster Walter; it seems the King's Men had allowed Walter to keep a small amount to be shared among those of our fraternity who did not immediately flee the abbey. This was barely enough to pay for his keep and shelter on the road, but the merchants were generous and asked no questions. (Brother Vincent had borrowed clothes from one of the lay servants, and did not reveal his identity as a religious.) He told me in a letter he believed God willed him to live on to do good in the world rather than to risk his life as a dispossessed religious, for he learned that throughout England there was both sympathy and scorn for monks from destroyed monasteries. So after two days' travel he reached a village where his travelling companions stopped at an inn to spend the night. Vincent was uneasy about staying at an inn among drunkards and women, fearing he might be tempted to commit a mortal sin. But the merchants persuaded him, and there was good food and ale which he enjoyed greatly as Lent was over. And at this inn – the Leathern Bottle, he called it – he heard talk about a neighbouring village where their much-loved priest had died suddenly. In such troubled times there was fear no priest could be found to take his place.

Next day Vincent said farewell to his fellow travellers, claiming that he was bound for Northampton, for he had heard that the shrine of Our Lady at Walsingham had been closed down. And he made his way on foot to the village without a priest; which I later learned is called Yewstoke. He told me that his heart sang as he came over a hill and saw its small grey church, smoke rising from the clustering cottages, sheep and cattle grazing on the common; at once he knew God had led him there. (You will recall, Robert, that Vincent is a man of great faith and confidence in Our Lord.) This is all I know at present, but instinct tells me Brother Vincent will fare well in his new life. The villagers are blessed to have him as their pastor.

As for myself, I am well looked after and want for nothing in worldly goods: as a member of our Cistercian Order possessions have never been important to me. Yet I must admit to a constant longing to be back at our beloved Abbey again, as it was, with all its rituals, the Daily Office, the fellowship of the Brethren, our quiet and ordered lives. There was a pattern, a framework, which I sorely miss. This longing does not get any less. I am ashamed at my discontent when others of our community have suffered so much more. God has been good to set me down in this peaceful place, among not unfriendly people and much that is familiar – and I owe heartfelt thanks to you, Robert, for guiding me here. Do not think I am ungrateful; but as I get older the loss of all that Dorsley meant to me seems harder to bear.

Come back soon, dear Robert, and let me continue as your father confessor, though all unworthy – Leo.

XVII

FAR FROM THE WORLD, THE FLESH AND THE DEVIL

*A brother may be assigned a burdensome task or something he cannot do.
If so, he should with all gentleness and obdience accept the order given
him......trusting in God's help, he must in love obey.*

The rule of St Benedict, chapter 68

I used to believe that my sanctuary here at the Deer Park would be a place of utter peace and quiet, with few visitors and no untoward happenings. I did not expect it to become almost a place of pilgrimage, nor that so many old and new friends would bring their troubles to me. Who am I to disentangle worldly tangles?

The bees, the geese and the fish keep me occupied. Lady Poyntz and Lady Felicity, when they visit, concern themselves with my welfare; Sir Nicholas gives orders to his servants to see to my daily needs, few as they are. Old friends from Dorsley keep in touch. And these are the folk who seem to regard me as some kind of spiritual comforter, a task surely for Our Lord alone. I earnestly beg them not to look to me for divine guidance, yet they keep coming. My life here seems far removed from the satisfaction of serving the Dorsley community, providing so many of their daily needs (save for bread and ale) and living the collective life of prayer and manual labour. But I must not cultivate discontent and frustration. In spite of all, God is good to me, and I must strive to serve him in whatever way I can.

First there is the happy ending to Brother Wilfrid's story: but I suppose I must not call him Brother now.

He rode to the Deer Park the other day; he tells me it is barely a three-day journey from Tintern by horse, crossing the Severn on the ferry between Chepstow and Bristol. After this he rode across country to avoid any who might still be searching for renegade monks. And he brought with him bread and flat cakes he had made with flour ground at his new mill, the Mill-By-The-River-Usk. He looked fit and contented, perhaps a little stouter. So pleased I was to see him I did not at first notice the woman following him in a kind of litter slung between two horses.

"Brother Leo, my dear old friend, God's blessing be upon you."

"And God be with you also, my dear Wilfrid. How goes it with you?"

"Exceedingly well, God be thanked. And here to meet you is my newly-wed wife, Mistress Bronwen. Please give us your blessing, Brother. However I may have sinned in the past – and I do not ask you to forgive my shortcomings – it will mean so much to us both to have you bless our union."

My surprise could not have been greater: I fear it showed. A homely middle-aged woman with a kind face, but only a few words of English, for – as I soon learned – she is Welsh born and bred. None theless I did my best to make her welcome; I showed her my bees and the small fish pond I have constructed at the foot of the hill. It seemed a wedding present would be appropriate, so I gave her a basket of apples, a flask of honey and some eggs from my geese.

The geese are a recent addition to my small farm: my friend the beekeeper brought me three goslings just hatched, and I kept them safe in a kind of ark made of tree branches till they were big enough to fend for themselves. Now they are quite independent, grazing freely in the park – needless to say they must not be allowed to do damage in my Lady's garden. They feed just on grass, they lay their eggs where they are easy to find, and at night they return to the ark. Some folk dislike their honking, but it gives me warning of anyone coming. My one anxiety is that foxes and rats are very fond of geese, but so far none have attacked them.

Mistress Bronwen made signs of pleasure at the presents, and Wilfrid even more so. They are clearly devoted to each other, and he brought her all this way to meet me and receive my benediction. This I must take as a great compliment.

From the diary of Susannah, wife to Sir Nicholas Poyntz

At the Deer Park, Monday June 12, 1538

On this day I arrived from London to oversee arrangements for guests attending our deerhunt next week. There will be a party of 14, not including ourselves, and I wish everything to be just so. The Throckmortons will use the guest room and may stay overnight. Sir John Hilliard is bringing a party of five over from Tetbury, and the Spendloves with their two sons are coming at midday from Oxford. That leaves Lady Felicity's parents and her brother; she may join them although the dear girl knows she is welcome by my hearth at any time, deerhunt or no deerhunt.

First I asked our head forester to make sure there would be seasoned timber enough for fires in all the rooms and for a venison roast enough to satisfy everyone. Next to the roof, to see there is no danger for guests going up there to watch the chase; and so down to the banqueting chamber: seating for 16, finger bowls and all the best pewter out.

During the feast I like to have music, perhaps a lute and a recorder, so it was necessary to remind Nicholas to bring the musicians with him from London as we do not have resident music-makers here. I shall choose the music, perhaps something by Mr Purcell or Mr Tallis, and we might even have a harpist. Mr Farmer's madrigal of "Fair Phyllis I saw sitting alone" is always a popular tune. After we have all eaten well and enjoyed each other's company there may be a small entertainment, a charade or the like.

The main part of the preparation is to talk to the cooks and give directions for the deer roast. The venison must be well hung but still fresh, dressed with spices and served with some of Father Leonardo's sweet vegetables. I must see that he is well, and ask him about fruit and honey for desserts. Nicholas will attend to the wines. Whilst I am occupied with all this the servants tell me a young man and a young woman, in travelling clothes, are asking for me. I am not expecting any other than the invited guests; it is not at all convenient.

Greatly to my surprise it is Felicity who is shown into the reception room, and with her a young man I have seen now and then working around the stables.

"My dearest godmother, forgive this intrusion. I know how busy you must be, but I need to speak to you before my parents arrive – they are on their way."

"Felicity sweetheart, you are always free to come and go here, as you know. Is this something that cannot wait?"

"My lady, you may not have met Robert Woodward – he sometimes helps the grooms here."

I found myself regarding a good-looking young man with quite a courtly manner, and when he spoke it was not as I would expect a servant to speak.

"Lady Poyntz, I beg you to forgive my unannounced entrance. Felicity – Lady Felicity – has told me of your kindness and compassion, so we come to throw ourselves at your feet with a special plea."

I had not the faintest idea what lay behind all this, but something about their urgent and troubled manner caught my attention.

"Please, both of you, be seated, and tell me what is distressing you."

"My dearest godmother, you are the first person to know this. Robert and I love each other, and we wish to be married."

At first I could hardly believe what I was hearing, but gradually the picture became clearer. My favourite Felicity, from one of the noblest families in the land, in love with a groom? And one of the Old Faith? And marriage? Without her parents' knowledge? A marriage between a Protestant noblewoman and a Catholic serving-man?

We talked for an hour, even though I was deep in preparations for the feast. The two young people persuaded me they were genuinely in love and not so ill suited as I had feared at first. But I needed time to consider: should I tell her parents? Should I consult Nicholas? How could I give my blessing to such a union , planned covertly without the blessing of my oldest and dearest friends? Felicity is not in truth my niece, rather my goddaughter, but I have always thought of myself as her aunt, and treated her as a member of my family.

In the midst of this confusion it occurred to me that I might seek the wisdom of Father Leonardo, since I was on my way to consult him about his fruit and vegetables and honey for the feast. Of course he would respect my confidence and offer wise advice.

To my utter astonishment Brother Leonardo (I must not call him Father, for he is neither priest nor abbot) revealed that he knew both the lovers well. Felicity it seems has been in the habit of bringing him small presents and chatting with him whenever she visits here. And this lad Robert – this was hardest of all for me to understand – comes from a decent glovemaker's family and was once a novice monk at Abbey Dorsley with Leo. Now he earns a kind of living as a groom and valet, not so much in the stables as in respectable households such as ours. Brother Leonardo went so far as to advise me he believed they would be very happy together, and that he would talk to them both separately before he formed an opinion . Meanwhile Felicity would watch the deer chase with her parents, saying nothing to them until Leo and I had discussed her problem further. It is the thought of my dear god-daughter marrying into the Old Faith that troubles me. And she is so young.

Tuesday June 13, 1538
We have had our deer chase and feast and all went well. The day was fine, the deerhounds in good form, and ten fullgrown stags were brought down. To those who say such noble beasts do not deserve

such a fate I say – the herd must be culled at certain seasons, and the foresters are careful that does and hinds are not endangered. It is without any doubt a magnificent spectacle, and all those who witnessed the chase marvelled at the speed and grace of deer and hounds alike. Those of us of a more nervous disposition did not see the kill. Nicholas was well pleased with the chase, and the Throckmortons and Spendloves (who have experience in the sport) complimented him warmly on the way the hunt was organised.

Twelve of us sat down to feast on the venison (Sir John and Lady Hilliard were obliged to hurry back to Oxford) and there was much good company and merriment. I was glad we had music to accompany our banquet. Late in the evening the other guests said their farewells, while Felicity and her parents spent the night here. I did not sleep well, being most anxious about the young couple and their future.

XVIII

UNIONS AND REUNIONS

There was a poor man who had one cow; and he heard his priest preach from the Gospel that God would increase a hundredfold what was given to him. So the poor man gave his cow to the priest, who blessed him and added the good man's cow to the others that he had. But it came about that the good man's cow came home to his house, bringing with her all the priest's cows too.

Michael of Northgate, the Ayenbite of Inwit,
The Prick of Conscience 1340

It was a little over two years since we had all left Abbey Dorsley in such distress and disorder.

I had made a new life for myself at the Deer Park, not without some guilt that my way had been easier than many of my brethren. Now there was to be a gathering, arranged for the most part by Robert. I had tried to persuade him that neither the place nor the time were a wise choice; but who could ever persuade Robert against his inclinations?

It had been a cold November, the leaves falling early, the bees and the smaller wild animals hibernating against the unseasonally sharp frosts, the birds needing seeds and berries already. (Yes, I did sometimes feed the wild birds, and Lady Poyntz teased me – not Brother Leonardo, but Saint Francis, she called me.) My cave (near enough a hermit's cell) was warmer for the long nights and sunless days by virtue of some sheep's wool blankets my friend the shepherd's wife had made, spinning and weaving the cloth herself. The smaller blankets were for bedding, over a mattress of straw, and the bigger ones she had hung around the cave to make a kind of tent. With all this and a candle lamp, enclosed for safety, as well as a fire of dry branches, kept always burning just outside the cave entrance, I was pretty comfortable.

I cannot truthfully say I suffered for our Lord as true hermits do. All kinds of people brought me gifts of food, drink and their friendship. I repaid them as best I could, with honey or vegetables, so long as I had a surplus beyond what the Poyntzes required. I was allowed to gather firewood in the park, and sometimes to collect scraps thrown out from the kitchen of the great house – these last to feed the wild animals and birds. Deer, rabbits, badgers and foxes came near the cave to feed. After a time I could recognise some, and they would respond to my call. We had I know not how many varieties of birds in the park, songbirds, predators and some migrants too – the swallows were a joy when they came in April, and I grieved to see them leave for warmer regions in the autumn.

This way of life pleased me; solitary but not too solitary, living frugally but not too frugally, having company some days and not others, still able to be in touch with some of my old colleagues. And of course saying the Daily Office.

Others tell me that I have followed the way of life of the Hermit Richard, who lived and wrote his wonderful homilies in Yorkshire about 100 years ago. But I do not profess to compare myself with such a great man and scholar. Fame is not something I aspire after.

So it came about that Wilfrid the miller sought me out. He was travelling secretly from the great abbey of Tintern, across the river, to visit his old parents because he had heard his mother was very ill, and one night he asked me to find him shelter; he believed his life would be still in danger if the King's men knew where to find him. The

Poyntzes were in London and I foresaw no danger if he slept in the Deer Park stable. I urged him to stay here again on his way back. Dear old Wilfrid, impulsive as ever, warm of heart and loud of voice. I was sad to learn from him that Tintern had been closed down, though comparatively peacefully, and its community broken up, though some of them still sheltered in villages nearby. The land has been granted to Earl Henry of Worcester, who as yet shows no inclination to tear down the buildings. But not much of value inside is left – no gold or silver plate, no coloured glass, no lead. The twelve monks who had not fled were given reasonable pensions, (eight pounds a year, or so I heard) and Abbot Gerald three times as much. Wilfrid of course (bless him) was not one of the resident twelve, but he easily found work as a miller in the river valley.

Then came Daniel and the woman disguised as a boy; Daniel was waiting for calmer weather to cross the Channel back to France, and the girl – Sister Agnes, I suppose I should call her – had at last had news of her father and brother. They were in hiding in Ireland, and she was able to ride to her family home and pass on the good news. But she was restless, too uneasy to stay for more than a few days with her mother, and now like a nomad she roams here once more. I guessed it would be because she longed to see Robert Woodward again, and the most likely place to find him would be here at the Deer Park.

Brother Theodore our Infirmarian had heard where I was living, so he rode across country to visit me for old time's sake. He was staying with a priest in the area who was an old friend of us both – none other than Dorsley's assistant carpenter Brother Vincent , accepted into a parish where the priest had lately died. So they came here together.

And greetings came by hand of a messenger to the Poyntzes at Deer Park, bringing me word of our Obedientiaries now settled at the Abbey of Jumieges across the Channel: Guilbert de Rougier, our Prior, Walter Lefevre our Guestmaster, and Benoit the Chamberlain – all of them from France originally. So I was glad to hear they had taken up their vocation again, even thought it was with a Benedictine community and not our own beloved Cistercians.

Then, with all this coming and going, my own dear boy Robert arrived. And not alone.

Riding behind him, side-saddle on his horse, there was a woman, heavily veiled and hooded. She slipped from the horse and ran towards the house. I knew better than to pry into Robert's affairs – in his own good time he would tell me whatever he wished me to hear. So it happened over the bee skeps.

"Father Leo, I need to confess."

"Not to me, dear boy. I am not a priest. But tell me what is on your mind, by all means."

"I am in love."

"So much I guessed. But why the secrecy?"

"Because I think you would not approve, and because I know you are fond of Agnes."

"It is not for me to approve or disapprove. If your conscience allows this love, then God will bless it."

"You do not ask who I am in love with?"

"Ir is hardly my business, and in any case I would not be likely to know the lady."

"Lady she is indeed, and you certainly know her. I wish to marry Felicity."

I had not for a moment suspected this news. The shock was profound. Fond as I am of both these young people, it seemed to me at first a union that could not be blessed by God or man. I was silent, reflecting.

"You have nothing to say to me, Leo?"

"Robert, of course I wish the greatest possible happiness for you both. But is marriage a practical possibility? What of your parents, and Lady Felicity's, and her position at Court? Does Lady Poyntz know and sanction this?"

"You think we have not considered all aspects? Leo, we love each other, and they say love triumphs over all obstacles."

There was nothing more I could say, except to give him my blessing. But I was troubled, not least because of Agnes.

When I saw Robert and Lady Felicity together later I could not doubt the depth of their love. Even I, an old man and a celibate, could sense the current flowing between them. Her eyes glowed and he held her hand as if he were afraid of losing her. When they looked at each other face to face I felt moved to tears.

It was Felicity herself who startled me most of all.

"Dear Father Leo, we have not told you quite everything. We want you to marry us, here at the Deer Park in your hermit cell, your special place. Then we will travel to the north of England, where I have relatives, and not embarrass you any more." She reached up and kissed me, and who could refuse such an appeal?

I explained to them both that I did not have authority to conduct a wedding, so such a ceremony would be illegal; that if it were discovered, terrible punishment might be visited on them. And even if I were an ordained priest and able to carry out the sacrament, I could not agree to do so without the permission of their parents. Lady Felicity I knew to be not yet of age, and I doubted very much if Robert's parents would agree to a clandestine marriage. The young people were persistent and did their best to talk me round to their way of seeing things. Finally I suggested an arrangement with a priest of the Old Faith (as they call it now) who might meet their wishes without too many questions. I was careful not to name him.

Again Felicity put her arms round me. "Dear Father Leo, we have still not told you everything. I am carrying Robert's baby, and we would not wish the child to be born out of wedlock. Now will you say yes?"

She kissed me, and of course I could not resist her pleading. Perhaps I am weak.

The story is taken up again by Daniel

For a few weeks Agnes and I have been content to stay at the Deer Park, among my old Dorsley friends. Much sympathy has been shown to me over the terrible loss of Septimus; indeed Brother Leo and Brother Wilfrid set up a Requiem Mass for him in the chapel of a Catholic family mansion near here, and this was a great comfort to me. I have been in touch with Septimus's parents, and they invited me to stay with them, but I do not feel ready for this yet. I feel drawn to return to France to practise my art in conge-

nial surroundings, at least until it is safe to settle in England. The Catholic rituals are still allowed in English churches (though without statues, incense, holy water or displaying of holy relics) even though the king urges priests of the Old Faith to use an English translation of the Bible (there are several now, as well as Master Tyndale's) and Protestant forms of service. But I do not think this compromise will continue, whereas in France they have hardly heard of our reformation.

Agnes is deeply unhappy. She has been to see her mother, and set up a discreet communication between the Farrells in Worcestershire and Agnes's father and brother taking refuge in Ireland. She is very devout, observing the daily Office and thanking God for the present safety of all her family. But she has made it quite clear to me and to Brother Leo that she does not intend to resume her vocation.

"Sister Hildegarde no longer exists. The past is the past."

"So will you come to France and work for the Benedictines as a lay servant? Your sacred embroidery is a great gift which shouldn't be wasted."

"Daniel, I wish I could be single-minded as you are. Of course I must carry on with my needlework. But there are just now too many distractions; I have too many ungodly thoughts and desires."

I am afraid she is thinking still of Robert Woodward. We have not discussed the subject, but she cannot hide her feelings when she encounters him at the Deer Park, and to me it is sadly obvious he does not return her attachment. It distresses me to see her so unhappy, and not be able to offer her any comfort.

Yesterday, because of my increasing anxiety, I raised the matter with Brother Leo. He is wiser than any of us; he understands young people and their emotions. If anyone could bring Robert and Agnes together, it is Leo.

His response surprised me very much.

"Daniel, I am saying this in the full confidence that you will not repeat this to anyone, least of all to Agnes. Robert is in love with another woman, and he has asked me to arrange his marriage."

I could not begin to think how Agnes would receive this news. I find it shocking myself, that Robert should seem to transfer his affections so quickly and secretly after knowing Agnes for most of their lives. Bu there it is: they have never been lovers, rather brother and sister as far as he was concerned. I am wondering who is going to break the news to Agnes, when and where.

Meanwhile other news of a happier romance. Brother Wilfrid has left the desecrated abbey at Tintern to take over a mill farther up the river Usk, where the miller has died and left a family to be provided for. And Wilfrid tells us he will marry the widow and make his home with her and her children! Now this is amazing indeed. He is no youngster, and not (I would have said) a woman's man by anyone's judgement . But I can see how convenient it may be for them both, and after all a monk's life is a lonely life outside the cloister, as I am beginning to see. We all sincerely hope he will be happy with his Bronwen (she is Welsh, he tells us.)

My own future is very undecided, but I may return to Jumieges as a lay brother to carry on with my manuscripts and see if the Benedictine life style will suit me. If only Septimus were alive to advise me as he always did. I miss him more than ever.

XIV

PROMISES AND RESOLUTIONS

Love is the sweetest thing that man on earth has tasted;
Love is God's darling; love binds blood and bone...
For me and my loving love makes both be one

Richard Rolle of Hampole, *Love is Life*, c. 1320

I am growing to love the Deer Park in late summer, when the deer come near to the house to graze and owls call on still moonlit nights. I feel more at home here now than in London, and the garden is beginning to be a special joy. Brother Leonardo has many gifts: creating a garden for pleasure and produce, for food and flowers, is perhaps his greatest talent, and certainly given him by God. He is such a modest man, his requirements so frugal, that it almost embarrasses me to ask anything from him.

Our physic garden is growing well, and I am able to cull marjoram and thyme, lovage and pennyroyal, and even lungwort which they say cures chest pains. To draw the bees and the butterflies we have borage and comfrey, lemon balm and yarrow, which is good for my complexion if I make a mask of soaked herbs. Elderflower too clears the skin. For the house I make a pot pourri mixture of rose petals, lavender and juniper to hide any stale damp odours, and herb sachets to sweeten the pillows of our guests.

Nearer the house is the knot garden, which I helped Brother Leonardo to plan: as it develops we can see a pattern of diamonds and squares made by miniature hedges of clipped box and winter savory, and now his latest gift to me – tiny herbs shaped to make the entwined initials N and S, for Nicholas and Susannah. Thyme and creeping chamomile make up the letters. What prettier compliment could I ask?

Lately he has invited me to the orchard to pick some of the ripening fruit, quinces and medlars. Of course most of the crop is picked into wicker baskets by the servants, to store for the winter, but it is a real joy to pick straight from the tree and eat juicy pears.

As I said, I can hardly bring myself to seek favours from a man who does so much to please me. But on a dry crisp day in September I went to him with a troubled mind, troubled about the ever-growing love between my dear god-daughter Felicity and the groom Robert. Felicity had confided in me, and I sensed that Brother Leonardo knew about their hopes. They came to see me separately, and if ever I saw two young people in love it is these two. But I am troubled on two counts: what will my dear friends, Felicity's parents, say to such an ill-omened match? Not only are they from very different homes, but of opposed faiths. And I know my friends have quite another husband in mind for their only daughter. So I went quietly to seek Leonardo's advice, and I realised quickly he knew as much as I did.

"Father, you are the wisest man I know. Can any good come of this doomed relationship?"

"My daughter, their future is not in our hands, but in the hands of God. I have a high regard for Robert – remember I knew him well in the monastery – and I am certain he will make a loyal and caring husband. Whether he can afford to keep Lady Felicity in the comfort she has been used to in her own home, I cannot say. I believe she loves him enough to endure poverty with him, but how much and for how long is another matter."

"I very much fear Felicity's parents will do all they can to prevent this marriage. She has not yet told them she wants to marry a Catholic stable lad."

"Forgive me, Lady Poyntz. Robert is the son of a wealthy glover, well educated and skilled with horses – much more than a mere groom. Felicity has confessed to me that she has distant relatives in the north who will give them a home, and provide work for Robert, for the time being. I have tried to persuade her – but who am I to influence her? – to tell her parents her plans, even if she keeps her new home a secret."

"I agree with you absolutely. She must let them know if she marries. But who will marry them, and by what rites? Can you perform the ceremony for them, Brother Leonardo?"

"My lady, I am not able to. As you know, I am not a priest. And sadly I must suppose Lady Felicity will wish to marry according to the practices of the Protestant church."

So our conversation continued, both of us looking for ways to smooth the path of these young people whom we loved, but both of us deeply uneasy at the course of action they were planning.

For a day or two I was occupied with the latest deer hunt, Nicholas bringing friends from Court who must be regally entertained, leaving me little chance to speak privately to Felicity. Everything went well; a successful chase, two stags in their prime brought down, a venison feast even my ambitious Nicholas could be proud of. As a host he leaves nothing to chance, and he is so anxious to please his friends, those who (I believe) have even more influence at Court than he has. The king is getting old, and the future for all his courtiers when he dies is uncertain.

When the guests had left, and the day before she was to return to London, Felicity found me in the small parlour next to our banqueting room.

"My dearest godmother, I have a very great favour to ask."

"My dear girl, you know there is almost nothing I would not do for you. But what I suspect you are about to ask may be exceedingly difficult."

"It is this. As I think you know, Robert and I wish to marry. We shall do this very privately – I would not ask even you, dearest aunt, to condone something you may regard as sinful. We hope to find a village church with a priest who will marry us secretly according to the rites of the Catholic church – for our Protestant ceremony is not so very different under the present law, though Robert will have to accept the absence of holy water and statues, as well as candles and music. The favour I am asking, dearest kinswoman, is after the ceremony to tell my parents we are married. Will you do this *for me* ?"

"Felicity, will you not wait a while to reflect and perhaps talk this over with wiser advisers than me?"

Her answer, when it came, was like a blow to my heart. In a moment we were both in tears.

"I cannot wait. I am carrying Robert's child, and I would not wish it to be born out of wedlock."

Later I know Felicity and Robert went together to Father Leonardo to ask for his help, and this I believe he gave, though not with an easy mind.

The Feast of St Michael and All Angels, 29 September, 1539

On this day Robert Woodward and Lady Felicity Drummond came at daybreak to me, Father Vincent, once Brother incense maker and carpenter at Dorsley Abbey, now priest in charge of the parish church of St Edmund the Martyr in the Cotswold village of Yewstoke, to be married.

The good local people hereabouts have accepted me as their priest and pastor in view of my priestly vocation, and in spite of my long career as a Catholic monk. This is a devout community, hardworking farmers and craftsmen, who loved and missed their village priest Oswald when he died. So it was not difficult for them to take me in. I still say the Latin Mass when I am alone, but for the sake of peace and to keep the law I use Master Tyndale's Bible and avoid all reference to the Saints except St Edmund King and Martyr. It goes without saying I long for the sweet smell of incense and the tribute of candles, for these were at the centre of my monastic life – but if these were re-introduced here it could mean serious trouble for the good people of

Yewstoke. And good people they are , coming to worship on days when they are not working, even those who cannot read and write (the majority) and looking after my material needs. In return I do my best to serve them as a village priest should, saying Mass daily, visiting the sick (a familiar task from my Dorsley days), teaching their letters and the Catechism to the younger ones (there is no church school within many miles), and burying the dead as need arises.

When I left Oxford as a classics scholar it did not occur to me to do other than enter the Cistercian Order. I supposed there would be scope for me to write a little, to teach a little Greek and Latin, to do some menial tasks for Our Lord. An uncle introduced me to Abbot Godfrey, and after taking my vows I felt at once part of the community at Dorsley. Gradually I learned the crafts of incense mixing and candle making. The magical oils, the spices and herbs came from the East, some from the Holy Land; I did not question how. My task was to grind the crystals or powders, rubbing them through a sieve, then to mix them with perfumed oils, getting the proportions exactly right. At the Abbey they had a secret recipe handed down for many generations. We used chiefly sandalwood, from an evergreen tree grown in India, myrrh or gum resin from the Holy Land, and pure frankincense or gum olibanum, mainly from trees that grow on the coast of Arabia. The oils and spices I had to heat to a very high temperature in the thuribers, over charcoal chips. The chips were brought to us regularly by charcoal burners from the Forest of Dean, much nearer home than the source of the other ingredients.

The last stage involved mixing all the ingredients by hand in a wooden tray; leaving the mix to dry, and measuring out just enough for each glass phial – these were brought to us by a travelling herbalist who otherwise sold the phials for medical purposes. Most of our incense we used ourselves, a small amount went to churches and priories too poor to concoct their own. The burning of incense went on all the time somewhere in the Abbey, the fragrant smoke curling up like prayers rising. Here I miss greatly the warmth of those holy fragrances, and the joy of mixing them.

Our candles were made from beeswax, and Brother Leo provided it. I would visit his orchard and marvel at the huge numbers of bees in his charge. He would show me the way the bees produced yellow wax to form their honeycomb cells, and after the honey had been drained out the wax would harden to be shaped into candles. Goodness knows how many candles the Abbey would burn in a month – an enormous number – and I have no idea how we would have managed but for Leo's industrious little creatures.

So it was Leo who heard of my new vocation, and trusting to our old friendship he sent Robert and Felicity to me with a written prayer that I would help them. I agreed to perform the more or less forbidden sacrament of the Latin marriage rite at the behest of my old Dorsley friend, and because the young people had come to plead their case with such evident sincerity and simplicity. I talked to them privately at length, and I was impressed that both this man and this woman shared a strong faith despite the conflicting allegiances of their families. If there had been any doubt in my mind, or a weakness in Brother Leo's advocacy, I would have refused. The dangers were obvious: that Felicity's noble parents would intervene to stop the ceremony, that other Churchmen might get to hear of this unorthodox union and seek to prevent it; even that the Bishop himself would obstruct the sacrament. What I was doing was against the new law of the land, but I believed God himself would sanction it.

On an autumn morning cloudy with a gentle mist a man and a woman rode along the track leading to a remote village, where squat stone cottages rose as if growing out of the ground, clustering round a church built in the same grey stone, and standing in the same place since the Norman Conquest. The village name was Saxon: the yew, one of England's native trees, and stoke, a settlement. Here country people had worshipped for at least 700 years, and who knows how many couples had been united before this altar in the traditional faith?

Two other persons rode behind them, cloaked and hooded as if to hide their identities. They left their horses tied to one of the ancient massive trees, the yews, that sheltered the village and its modest church. Crows called in the trees, a hare thumped the ground of the churchyard where crooked headstones leaned together, and a cloud of white doves settled on the church roof.

This was one of many Cotswold churches untouched by the Reformation because of its remoteness. Antiquarians believe the Saxons built it, later generations added a tower and a columbarium to house the doves. Then in the days of the Plantagenet kings a few glazed windows, a statue of the Virgin (now much defaced) in a niche at the west end, and a limestone baptismal font gave the place more dignity and a heightened sense of purpose.

The misty ride reminded Robert of the morning when without warning Thomas Cromwell's men had attacked Abbey Dorsley, three years earlier. His life had changed radically since that day. The dim silence of the tiny church – no candles, no chanting, no incense – gave extra solemnity to the ceremony. Father Vincent met them at the door, wearing only his white monastic habit. They walked inside under the awesome mediaeval carvings of Christ in Majesty, flanked by strange stone monsters guarding the doorway, and marvelled at the skill of the early stonemasons. They followed Vincent through the tiny chancel, with its low zigzag framed arches and graceful vaulting, troublingly reminiscent of the scriptorium at Dorsley, and so reached the small plain stone altar at the east end. Between the chancel and the sanctuary a spiral stone staircase led up to the dovehouse, its 40 nesting holes a home for the Biblical birds of peace.

The only light came from a narrow east window, yet it was enough. There was no longer an altar rail nor any statues or silver candlesticks as might have graced the sanctuary a few years earlier. Already Vincent was planning to carve some plain wooden candle-sticks and perhaps a simple crucifix; obects that would please God but not offend local worshippers leaning towards the New Faith.

Robert and Felicity had only the two witnesses required by the Church, both chosen for their sympathy and discretion, Brother Daniel and the former nun Sister Agnes. Brother Leo had given them his blessing but told them his conscience would not allow him to be present in the church ("But may God be with you both now and always.")

Robert and Felicity knelt at the altar, Daniel and Agnes stood a little to one side. Vincent took them almost in a whisper through what to Robert seemed a truncated and emasculated form of the service, the grand Nuptial Mass, which he'd heard often enough as a choirboy in Worcester.

Deus Israel conjugat vos; et ipse sit vobiscum, qui misertus est duobus unicis; et nunc, Domine, fac eos plenius benedicere te. Beate omnes qui timent Dominum: qui ambulant in viis eius.

They exchanged their vows privately, in a near whisper.

Lastly Vincent pronounced the traditional blessing of the nuptial Mass:

Ecce sic benedicetur omnis homo, qui timet Dominum; et videas filios filiorum tuorum, et pax super Israel.

He sprinkled the husband and wife with holy water, and then it was over. As they left the tiny church grotesques – grinning clowns, dragons, fabulous birds – stared down at them quizzically, but the white doves murmured a blessing. Inside and out the stonemasons had added comical faces, portraits perhaps of living people, on spouts and beams. Generations of villagers watched over the church. This was not the first secret wedding they had witnessed.

After making their muted farewells to Vincent, as well as to Daniel and Agnes, the married pair rode back to Leo's cell – whom they now regarded as a proxy father. With a few words he left them alone together in the sheltered clearing near his cave, where they had first made love. As man and wife now they came together no longer terrified at what they were doing, no longer fearing both secular and divine wrath, but clinging to each other in physical ecstasy as if no one else in the world existed. And this coupling was more wonderful even than when the child had been conceived.

Later Susannah Poyntz came briefly to this secluded part of Leo's domain – she always called it Father Leonardo's kingdom – to say goodbye and to promise all in her power to placate Felicity's parents. There was no one else to wish them godspeed.

Much later Leo was to recall the day with a kind of humble joy, accepting that by God's will he had brought together those whom God had joined for no man to put asunder. In retrospect his objections to the union seemed less valid. He was even able to laugh at himself: to think that he had doubted Robert's fidelity or his devotion to the faith of his fathers. In time he felt others could be told of the fate of their one-time fellow religious, happily and securely married, living in Lancashire and working as bailiff on a large and prospering estate.

When Felicity's daughter was born they wrote to Leo that she was to be called Leonarda, and this gave him even more joy. Robert's own family had come to accept Felicity as their daughter-in-law, the child had been baptised in the Catholic faith; the only bar to total happiness was the continued disapproval of the Drummond family, though Lady Poyntz cautiously acted as an intermediary, passing on messages from Felicity to her mother.

Leo's small hermitage became a shrine for former Dorsley worshippers to visit, a focal point for meetings and communications. All of them turned to him in times of joy or trouble, to confess or to share their experiences. Always he reiterated his own unworthiness and urged them not to treat him as a father confessor, yet still they came. Quietly he laboured on among his bees and poultry, in the orchard or the herb garden; and to the delight of Lady Poyntz he continually improved and enlarged her pleasure garden, so that she was proud to show it to guests and neighbours. It had grown and become more complex. Clipped yew bushes enclosed areas fashioned like rooms, and flower-lined walks led to a small fountain and a paved area for the noblewomen to sit and do painting or embroidery. The Poyntzes spent more time here now, and the Deer Park acquired a reputation for its landscape and its unconventional planting.

For Daniel and Agnes the next few months were a time of doubt and anxiety. Choices lay before them: whether to resume their vocations, or in Agnes's case to return to her family. The Farrell family now seemed permanently separated; there was a possibility of Agnes's mother joining her exiled husband in Ireland. Daniel had finally made his peace with Septimus's mother, who in her extreme distress had refused to speak to him for a year after the death of her son, believing irrationally that Daniel could have saved Septimus's life.

Pilgrims and fellow Cistercians came from France to stay near Leo, praising his reclusive way of life and offering prayers for his physical and spiritual health , assuring him that the Order approved all that he was doing. They hoped he might rebuke himself less in the light of such support. One visitor was Brother Benoit, once the chamberlain at Dorsley, now established at the Mother House in Citeaux.

It was Benoit, being French and far more worldly wise than Leo, who suggested to Daniel and Agnes (though at different times) that they both might find a new or renewed vocation at Abbaye Jumieges. Travelling around France and visiting other communities, he was aware that Jumieges had a great need for talented illuminators and skilled embroideresses, and that men and women with these gifts might be attached to the abbey as lay workers, earning a living but partly subject to the disciplines of the monastic community. First Daniel and then Agnes agreed to this compromise by which they might use their gifts for God, but without wholly committing themselves to an Order which was somewhat alien to their former communities.

Like Robert and Felicity before them, they came to Leo for advice and blessing, and treasured his parting commendation: "My brother and sister, go out into the world and use your talents wisely, but never forget the disciplines in which you served". And as those two left England, travelling with an escort of lay brothers from Jumieges, it seemed to Leo that all the living survivors from Dorsley had found a way forward, one way or another, in this confused new world they now inhabited. He alone felt troubled that he was untrue to his vocation, and uncertain what path to follow.

DORSLEY REVIVIFIED SUMMER 1546

Bare ruined choirs where late the sweet birds sang ...

Shakespeare, *Sonnet* LXXIII, *c.* 1590

This last year of the reign of King Henry VIII, 1546, is one of the most peaceful of his turbulent years on the throne. It is said that his sixth wife, Katharine Parr, has brought him true happiness, and his relations with his European fellow monarchs (though not with the Pope) are relatively stable.

In Germany the great reformer, Martin Luther, has this year died in his bed. In England the Bibles of the martyred Tyndale, and his assistant Miles Coverdale (his version printed in Zurich and well received) are widely read in churches. Handwritten copies of Tyndale's Bible had to be smuggled into England, but in the last few years of his reign Henry has allowed three translations to be printed on the presses recently imported from Germany: those of Coverdale, John Rogers (called Matthew's Bible) and the Great Bible of 1539, chained in some of the more important churches. However the Old Faith survives – its flames to be violently fanned soon by Henry's Catholic daughter Mary – until these are cruelly put down in turn by his Protestant daughter Elizabeth. Some scholars are working on vernacular prayer books, though these will not be authorised until Henry's son Edward reigns briefly over England. Educated laypeople now can read the Scriptures for themselves and hold Communion with God without the intervention of a priest. England is changing.

Throughout the land a few ancient undestroyed abbeys are transforming themselves into cathedrals, as at Gloucester, or shrinking into parish churches, as at Malmesbury. In other places the ruins have become centres for occasional open air worship, as at Glastonbury, where Abbot Stephen Whiting had been hanged for resisting the seizure of his monastery. Believers still gather to see the twice-yearly flowering of the miraculous Glastonbury Thorn, and this has been popularised through a recent poem, The Lyfe of Joseph of Arimathea. Travelling men of religion set up services according to one or another rite, and devout local people creep back discreetly to hear the Mass where their fathers did. Protestantism may be the official religion, but Catholicism is far from quenched.

It is August 1546. On a mild late summer day a few would-be pilgrims and small clusters of faithful people are straggling across the Cotswolds towards a site they remember, or have heard talked about, or are curious to see. Some of them walk barefoot, in the way of pilgrims, carrying staves and missals, while others, booted, march more purposefully. From time to time they sing as they walk, or recite psalms: *Dominus pastor meus* is a favourite. A few carry wooden crosses, or banners with Biblical symbols. They follow well worn tracks, not paying much attention to other travellers, and pausing for rest and refreshment when they will. From time to time these groups are joined by curious observers.

Leading this motley and disorganised procession, a hundred or so strong, are two elderly men in white habits. Once they held high office in their monastery, now they travel incognito and with a certain humility. As they walk they converse in French, possibly so that their fellow travellers will not understand them.

169

"Ten years ago I would have said this journey was impossible. We would have been set upon, or forbidden to go this way. Our lives would have certainly been at risk, Brother, unless we were in disguise. I marvel that you and I have lived to tell the story, or that people still stop to hear it."

"England is a different place today. At present she enjoys the blessing of tolerance, however little and however briefly. The fact that we are here at all says much for changed attitudes. We can walk the roads with less fear, and good people are not afraid to offer us shelter overnight. Old friends who once led enclosed lives can come and go unhindered. Some we know well even have parish livings and live in secular communities. Lay people all over Europe can hear the Bible read in their own language. All this in little more than ten years since we were driven out, mark you."

Another couple, a young man and his wife, dressed modestly but speaking in a sophisticated manner, share bread and ale with their fellow walkers.

"Please take what you wish. We have more than enough for our needs. No, no, we ask for no payment, but maybe you can answer some questions that are puzzling us. We've been abroad for some years. This Reformation and the New Learning, what difference have they made to ordinary people?"

The reply comes from a husky man carrying a blacksmith's tools.

"Next to no difference, mistress. We goes to church and reads our Bibles and does what parson tells us much as we always did. But in my town we were ordered to close down our chantry chapel or turn it into a school."

"Why would they make you do that?"

"Well, they tells us prayers for the dead are – what is it? – a super-stitious practice. Myself, I think schools for the living are a sight more useful. The young ones learn more in schools than they ever learned in church. And learn it in English, too. Keep Latin for the churches, I say, if they want it. No harm in having the Bible or the Prayer Book in English, till those in high places tells us otherwise."

A single man, a parish priest by his robe, walks alone carrying an illuminated book. When they stop to eat he turns to his neighbour.

"I've not been back to this part of England for nearly ten years, and I see many changes in the woods and pasture land. More crops, fewer sheep, bigger villages. This abbey I believe we all are making for – what happened to it?"

"You truly have not heard? First the King's Men came and destroyed the abbey and killed the good Abbot when he tried to drive them out. Then some of the stone was robbed to build a grand house over towards Bath: they say it's a fine place. All the abbey land was carved up among favourites at court, they say. Merchants and townsmen came to collect the lead and coloured glass, carted it away by the wagonload. I've also heard say some of the old monks still live as hermits hereabouts, but I don't know if it's true. I'm on my way to the abbey because it used to be a good holy place, with good holy men living there, and I reckon it should be built up again if that's possible. We surely need holy places in England today."

Joining the straggle of walkers, not all of them obvious pilgrims or sightseers, an older man in a monastic habit offers help to travellers with sore feet or aching backs. They thank him in some embarrassment, not sure if they should offer payment.

"No, no, my brothers and sisters, this is no hardship for me, and years ago I looked after the sick in a religious community hereabouts. This journey is a return to old times and I'm glad to find I haven't entirely lost the knack of offering a little first aid on the way. Come and let me rub some ointment on your feet, good people."

"You know the place we're all making for, father?"

"Indeed I knew it well once. A holy place with a holy man in charge of it. Some of us are gathering there today to do honour to his memory and to raise a memorial to him."

"But we hear the place is just a ruin?"

"Not altogether a ruin. A place that still speaks of the past, a spiritual place. The nobleman who owns the land now has given us permission to hold this gathering and put the abbey to worship again, this one time. Moreover he has promised us there will be no more desecration of the buildings; they will be preserved for others after us. It's our hope the sight of these ruins will offer them true inspiration."

" So why are there so many of us on the road today?"

"I guess the Abbot is well remembered not only by religious like myself, but others who were given help or hospitality at the abbey. It was a place famed for good works. People have talked for years about coming together to put up a memorial and praise God one more time, as we – as they used to. *Laus Deo*, neither the man nor the community are forgotten. There may be a hundred of us on our way there. That tells you how many believers are here to make a demonstration of their faith today."

As they topped a little rise they reached the edge of the escarpment, with a great river valley below them; and a mile or so off, beyond a bend in the river, the ruins, now roofless, of what had once been a complex of tall stone buidings. Some stonework was still recognisable as the remains of arches, window tracery, corbels. From above the travellers looked down on the square of a cloister garth, the cruciform layout of a church, other collapsed walls that might have sheltered a refectory, a chapter house, or a handsome gatehouse.

Trees and bushes now clothed the bare walls, and tracks made by sheep patterned the grass. The stones seemed to speak of history, of the faith of many who had lived and worked here, of a chapter not altogether closed. Farther off the travellers could see derelict barns, overgrown ponds and abandoned fields, but no human figure in sight.

The straggle of walkers stopped in amazement and whispered among themselves as if afraid to disturb the peace. Some crossed themselves and some prayed silently. Then they moved onward and downward, following a sheep track, as if at a hidden signal, to stand among the ruins and reflect on all that had happened in this place.

In later years the event came to be called Revival Day, marking the annual return to life for 24 hours of what had been Abbey Dorsley. The pilgrims – for that is what they were, however unofficially – grouped themselves in the ruin of the nave, looking towards the east end of the former abbey church, nave and chancel now a shell. A man's voice, unaccompanied, began to chant a psalm, and the crowd took it up. A man in a monk's habit read aloud from the Latin Bible, and soon they were following the liturgy of the Mass. There was no music and no one in authority to lead them, yet they seemed inspired and united in their spontaneous devotion. A slight wind sprang up, and a woman called out: "The Holy Spirit has come among us."

As the Mass came to an end they waited for the next happening. After a pause a monk climbed on to one of the damaged walls and addressed them all. "Brothers and sisters, we have come here to honour Godfrey of Verbier, God rest his soul. It is ten years since he was brutally killed in this holy place. He died for his faith, and some of us believe he will be canonised . In any case this was his home and a place where he exercised great spiritual authority. Those of us who were privileged to worship with him are anxious to see some kind of memorial to him set up, though this must be done with the utmost discretion so that we are not accused of idolatry. One of us has carved a stone tribute, and we ask if you would agree to this being kept in a safe place near the site of the abbey, to be brought out on this day each year. If you agree, you must pledge yourselves never to reveal its whereabouts to others not of our faith. Is it agreed?"

And a mighty shout went up from the crowd: "Consensus est!"

So Brother Joseph's carving of Abbot Godfrey, executed in his lifetime and secretly guarded over the years, was shown to the people and reverenced as the likeness of a martyr. In years to come a home would be found for it in a Catholic country house, then in a French monastery, and finally in a museum.

There was yet another surprise, some would call it a miracle, for the pilgrims – the first of many who would travel great distances to worship at Abbey Dorsley on this August day each year. And this too was an artefact most intimately connected with the abbey's history.

As the service ended a country boy, perhaps a farmer's son, came nervously up to the monk who held the carving.

"Sir, I have here a relic they say came to the abbey hundreds of years ago. It's been hidden in my father's barn since the day the abbey was destroyed. Shall I show it to you? Will the people be glad to see it?"

Walter the Guestmaster could scarcely believe what he was seeing: the tiny wooden image of the Virgin that, along with the scrap of lace from Our Lady's veil, had been the abbey's most revered sacred object. There was no mistaking the handiwork of the unknown craftsman who had fashioned it, so they said, in the 12th century as a gift for the founder: in plain olive wood brought from the Holy Land, worn by the hands of pilgrims, unmistakably the image of Our Lady of Dorsley.

When Walter identified the holy relic to the crowd, a great cheer went up. This for them was confirmation of their faith, a tangible and visible sign that God approved their keeping alive the memory of Abbey Dorsley and Godfrey of Verbier.

"What is your name, boy?"

"Sir, I'm Richard the Cooper's son. I live across there, by the river."

"Will you continue to guard this precious relic for us?"

"That would be too great a task. Our farm is not suited any longer to keeping Our Lady safe. Please take her to a place of safety."

"But where? Can anyone suggest such a place?"

Then an elderly monk who had been at the back of the crowd spoke up. "It would be an honour beyond all honours for me to look after Our Lady and reverence her every day. Can you trust me? Then all who wish can come secretly to worship her, but at other times she will be hidden where no one but I can see her. Will you trust me, Master Walter?"

"Leo! Why did you not tell us you were here? Walking so far, at your age – we are truly glad to have you with us. So many of us from the old days; Godfrey would have rejoiced, God rest his soul."

"And will you allow me to guard Our Lady of Dorsley?"

"Dear Brother, there is no one better qualified and no one I would rather entrust her to. Take and care for her as long as you have health and strength."

Leo knelt, and received reverently from Prior Guilbert the tiny wooden figure to be blessed in his hands. The boy Richard knelt too, and the Prior made the sign of the cross over him, promising him many blessings for his devotion in keeping the holy image hidden for so long. Other pilgrims thronged round, wishing to touch the sacred carving, believing that some of its holiness would be passed on to them. Monks and lay people, travellers and members of Richard's family thought they were witnesses to a miracle, one that would be talked of and prayed about for years to come. A shrine would surely spring up here, a place of official pilgrimage: the shrine of Our Lady of Dorsley.

Leo stood back a little until he was joined by a horseman, one who had not walked in the procession but watched from the other side of the valley. He led a second horse which Leo was persuaded to mount for the long journey back to the Deer Park, keeping safe under his monastic habit (for this he had never given up) the carved figure that meant so much to him. Gradually the crowd dispersed, not realising that they had given birth to an annual festival, the revival of Abbey Dorsley, but aware of a brightness in the evening sky, and the sound of unseen music.

ACKNOWLEDGEMENTS

I have read much material relating to the dissolution of the monasteries, and followed many guides round lovingly preserved ancient sites. My greatest pleasure has been in exploring pre-Reformation village churches and some of the great monastic ruins in the care of the National Trust, English Heritage, CADW (Welsh Historic Monuments) or Glastonbury Abbey Trust, in particular, Tintern, Hailes, Lacock and Glastonbury; or abbeys where worship still continues, as at Malmesbury, Tewkesbury, Gloucester, Prinknash and Sherborne. The initial inspiration for this story came from attending as a volunteer for the past five years at the Tudor hunting lodge of Newark Park, Wotton-under-Edge, which is the original Deer Park.